CONTENTS

He ty in

E N ING

W PS

R and POWER 98

new editi

This guidance is issued by the Health and
Safety Executive. Following the guidance is
not compulsory and you are free to take
other action. But if you do follow the
guidance you will normally be doing
enough to comply with the law. Health and
Safety Inspectors seek to secure
compliance with the law and may refer to
this guidance as illustrating good practice.

2004 Reprint

In general, the amendments included in this
reprint reflect updated publications and
regulations. The overall guidance has not
changed.

HSE gratefully acknowledges the help of
Elf Oil Industrial Lubricants Division in
the preparation of the cover illustration.

FOREWORD

This guidance has been written for people who run and work in small engineering workshops, ranging from those who

▼ make their own products,

to those who

▼ maintain and repair plant and machinery either independently or as part of larger enterprises.

It is intended to help them manage their own health and safety and work in safer and healthier ways.

As engineering is a wide ranging activity the booklet does not deal with every hazard which may arise or every precaution which can be taken. It does, however, outline the most serious and frequent hazards and the best ways of dealing with them.

The 'Further reading' section:

▼ lists HSE and other publications which give more detail on the subjects dealt with;

▼ provides information on other sources of help.

In this guidance:

> 'must' denotes a legal obligation; outlines of the law applying to engineering workshops are provided in lined boxes on a blue background just like this paragraph;

▼ 'do' and 'don't', 'should' and 'should not' and other recommendations such as 'use', 'fit' and 'prevent' represent good practice, which, if adopted, will usually be what is reasonably practicable in the given circumstances although there may be other legally acceptable ways of achieving the same objective.

▼ text in italics (where it is not a reference, sub-heading or caption) outlines requirements of Approved Codes of Practice which have been approved by the Health and Safety Commission and give advice on how to comply with the law. If you are prosecuted for a breach of health and safety law, and it is proved that you have not followed the relevant provisions of the Code, a court will find you at fault, unless you can show you have complied with the law in some other way

▼ tips on good practice are indicated by phrases such as 'think about' and 'consider'

▼ the early sections deal with how to tackle health and safety issues common to most engineering workshops; later sections deal with more specific activities which may not be carried on in all workshops.

MANAGING HEALTH AND SAFETY

Successful health and safety management in small engineering workshops is about identifying the most frequent and serious risks and adopting the right precautions, taking account of time, money and resources.

This book identifies how most serious accidents happen and how most ill health is caused in engineering workshops.

If you use machines or processes which are not described in this booklet, see where they are similar to those described and work out whether they pose the same hazards and whether the precautions suggested would be right, as well as seeking further advice.

THE MANAGEMENT OF HEALTH AND SAFETY AT WORK REGULATIONS 1999 *outlined*

Employers must:

■ assess risks to the health and safety of their employees and non-employees arising in, or from, the workshop, and review them when there is significant change. Records of significant findings of the assessment must be kept where there are five or more employees

■ plan, organise, control, monitor and review the preventative and protective measures taken as a result of the assessment

■ provide health surveillance where necessary (see page 20), for example to help control health risks from metalworking fluids

■ appoint any competent person(s) needed to help them comply with legal obligations, for example, when having lifting equipment thoroughly examined

■ set out what should be done in case of serious and imminent danger in the workshop, such as the spillage of a large amount of degreasing solvent

■ tell employees about the risks and precautions involved in their work

■ train employees to work safely.

You may need help beyond that given in this book. If you do, trade and employer associations, such as EEF - The Manufacturers' Organisation, the Manufacturing Technologies Association (for machine suppliers) or local Chambers of Commerce, offer a range of advice and support. These sources of information are given on page 81. HSE inspectors are always willing to help (see page 90 for HSE Office details).

Employers must also consult with all their employees (including self-employed workers classed as employed persons under health and safety law) on health and safety matters. This will involve not only giving information but also listening to and taking account of what employees say before any health and safety decisions are taken.

KEY REFERENCE: *Management of health and safety at work*
Approved Code of Practice L21   HSE Books 2000 ISBN 0 7176 2488 9

HOW MOST ACCIDENTS AND CASES OF WORK-RELATED ILL HEALTH ARISE

Accident and ill-health data for such a wide and varied sector is available from a number of sources, including published HSE material, research papers, industry statistics, and trade association and trade union publications, although it is difficult to see the whole picture. The interpretation of the available data in this booklet is based upon the experience of health and safety inspectors gained over many years in dealing with the sector.

ACCIDENTS AND ILL HEALTH

There are many thousands of accidents and cases of ill health reported every year in small engineering workshops. Almost two-thirds of all such accidents reported to HSE arise from the movement of people, goods and vehicles into, around and out of workshops. Of these 'movement' accidents:

▼ about half involve lifting and moving goods, and

▼ about half involve slips, trips and falls and hitting stationary or moving plant and equipment.

'Non-movement' accidents usually arise from the use of machinery; these account for between 10 and 15% of all accidents.

Electrical accidents are not uncommon and frequently have the potential for more serious injuries than those recorded.

The most common occupational diseases are dermatitis, deafness, asthma and vibration white finger, and back, hand, arm, shoulder and neck problems.

In any particular workshop **risks** which are relevant should be assessed. Those likely to be of most concern include:

▼ movement of people, goods and vehicles around the workshop, particularly manual handling

▼ machinery safeguarding

▼ hazardous substances, particularly metalworking fluids, degreasing solvents, and dust or fume from welding, brazing, soldering, coating and painting

▼ noise, and

▼ vibration.

Injuries in engineering industries as reported to HSE's Field Operations Directorate and local authorities 1998/99 - 2000/01

	Non-fatal		
	98/99	**99/00**	**00/01 (provisional)**
Total	*15 267*	*15 078*	*14 668*
of which main cause involved:			
Handling and carrying	5057 (33%)	4955 (33%)	4842 (33%)
Being struck (eg by falling objects, moving machinery)	2826 (19%)	2872 (19%)	2698 (18%)
Slipping and tripping	2318 (15%)	2386 (16%)	2349 (16%)
Machinery	1778 (12%)	1734 (12%)	1641 (11%)
Falls from height	935 (6%)	950 (6%)	910 (6%)
Workplace transport	331 (2%)	331 (2%)	360 (2%)

COSTS

The costs of accidents and ill health to small engineering workshops may be disproportionately high. Many employees are 'key' workers whose loss through injury or ill health severely disrupts production and lowers profitability.

IF YOU WANT TO START CHECKING CONDITIONS RIGHT AWAY USE THIS INSTANT ACTION CHECKLIST

CHECK	INSTANT ACTION	LONG-TERM SOLUTION
Are fixed machine guards in position and secured?	Replace discarded guards and secure them by a fixing which needs a tool to undo it.	If fixed guards are being removed for frequent access (more than once per shift) replace with interlocking guards.
Are interlocking guards fitted and working?	If not, restore or repair them.	Start a programme of preventative maintenance.
Are all work area and passageway floors in good condition, kept clear and free from tripping and slipping hazards?	Keep all areas tidy and clean, and avoid trailing leads. Repair holes in floors and clear up spillages.	Provide non-slip floor surfaces. Mark gangways. Train and instruct employees to keep workplace unobstructed.
Is anyone required to lift or carry heavy or bulky items and equipment unaided?	Mark each load with its weight and train all employees to lift and carry safely.	See how the job may be avoided. Provide mechanical aids where possible.
Are any employees suffering from dermatitis?	Get them to see their GPs and provide suitable gloves if these won't add to risks at machinery.	Try to remove the cause, eg redesign the work so that handling the source of contamination is avoided.
Do metalworking fluids smell unpleasant, particularly after a break from machining?	Replace with clean fluid, after cleaning the machine and sump.	Try to find and eliminate cause of contamination.
Is there a visible fume mist or haze in the workshop? Is there much visible dust from grinding, polishing or blasting?	Check existing controls and ventilation, remedy and, if necessary, improve general ventilation.	Prevent fume, mist, vapour or dust from being generated or capture it close to source before it can be breathed and remove it from the workshop.
If you can't hear someone 2 m away talking in a normal voice.	Make sure noise/machine enclosures are closed and hearing protection is being worn.	Assess, remove, reduce or enclose noise at source.
Are vibration levels of hand-held tools as low as possible?	Check suppliers' data on vibration levels. Keep equipment maintained.	Buy and use reduced-vibration tools wherever possible.
If all vehicles (including fork-lift trucks) and pedestrians are kept.	Ensure that all drivers on site are properly trained and fork-lift truck operators authorised. Enforce speed limits and reduce the need for reversing.	Review all transport movements, including delivery and customer vehicles. Consider one-way systems and clearly mark and sign traffic routes.

HOW TO USE THIS BOOK TO START YOUR RISK ASSESSMENT

Here are some questions for finding out how dangerous or unhealthy your workshop might be, and what to do about it.

GENERALLY

Think about the times when people have been off work recently:

▼ Could their absences be put down to conditions at work?

▼ Is there a pattern to any of them?

▼ Have the lessons of any recent accidents, near misses or cases of work-related ill-health been missed?

▼ Are there health or safety aspects of any processes/operations you feel uneasy about?

THE WORKSHOP ITSELF

Are there any parts which are:

▼ dirty

▼ dark

▼ obstructed

▼ poorly ventilated

▼ unnecessarily wet, or

▼ otherwise dangerous or unhealthy to move around or work in?

MOVING AND WORKING WITH ARTICLES BY HAND; LOADING/UNLOADING MACHINES; ASSEMBLY AND PACKING

Has anyone complained about or been off work with a bad back, or persistent hand, arm, shoulder or neck problems which could be put down to work?

What about the loads being moved?
Are they too:

▼ heavy

▼ sharp

▼ large

▼ awkward

▼ hot or cold?

Does the job involve a lot of frequent, forceful or awkward movements?

IF THE ANSWER IS 'YES'

Investigate the possible causes further. The most likely ones are outlined in this booklet.

See pages 8-9 for details of the standards required.

Complete the more detailed questionnaire on pages 92-93 (for lifting) and pages 94-98 (for handling). If you have problems, the solutions suggested on pages 12–17 may help.

VEHICLES (INCLUDING FORK-LIFT TRUCKS)

Is there any damage to the workshop or plant and machinery from vehicles?

Do vehicles operate close to pedestrians?

Are vehicles required to reverse?

Does anyone use vehicles without being properly selected and trained?

Are the conditions in which they operate too dark, obstructed, wet or otherwise dangerous?

METALWORKING - MACHINING AND WELDING

Is it difficult to hear someone talking (in a normal voice) 2 m away at any point in the workshop?

Is it possible to reach (**DON'T TRY!**) any pressing, shearing, rotating, cutting or sawing tools especially when: loading/unloading components; removing swarf; or making adjustments?

Is there any visible fume, dust, mist or spray, or can it be smelt?

Do some operators frequently have to manipulate or load/unload components which are too heavy, hot, awkward or sharp?

Do you machine, weld or work with components containing cadmium, lead, chrome or similarly hazardous substances?

Do employees complain about numb or tingling fingers, 'dead hands' on cold days or finger blanching.

CLEANING AND FINISHING

Do you use:

▼ a vapour degreaser?

▼ other means of degreasing?

Do you paint components, or use coating powders?

IF THE ANSWER IS 'YES'

This may indicate too fast/careless driving or a poorly laid out workplace and also potential for injuries. Investigate further.

See pages 18-19 for advice on the selection and training of drivers.

See pages 8-9 for the minimum standards required for workshops.

Carry out a noise assessment - pages 38-42 tell you how to do this and make the most of it and how to reduce and control excessive noise.

See the individual machining sections of this booklet, pages 44-59, for advice on how to guard machinery.

Viewing any suspected source with a strong light (eg a Tyndall beam or video light) behind it will show where the fume is. See pages 20-22 on how to avoid or control harmful fume, dust, mist and spray. See pages 99-100 for guidance on checking the health of people working with metal cutting fluids.

See pages 12-17 for advice on lifting and handling.

See pages 20-22 for advice on how to control exposures to hazardous substances.

See page 43 for advice on how to deal with hand-arm vibration.

See pages 61-62 for how to maintain it and prevent the need to get in and clean it.

See page 60 for how to avoid and control exposures to harmful cleaners.

See pages 69-73 for how to avoid and control exposures to harmful substances in paints and coating powders.

FOR A LONGER LOOK,
TAKE 5 STEPS TO YOUR RISK ASSESSMENT

The Five Steps

▼ Look for the hazards

▼ Decide who might be harmed and how

▼ Evaluate the risks and decide whether precautions are adequate or more should be done

▼ Record your findings

▼ Review you assessment from time to time and revise it if necessary

---

Using the information on the preceding pages and the rest of this booklet, identify:

POSSIBLE HAZARDS (CHANGE AND/OR INSERT YOUR OWN AS NECESSARY)

WHO MIGHT BE HARMED

HANDLING

TRANSPORT and VEHICLE MOVEMENTS

METALWORKING FLUIDS

CLEANING and DEGREASING SOLVENTS

MACHINERY (including setting and maintenance)

WELDING PROCESSES and MATERIALS

NOISE

VIBRATION

YOUR RISK ASSESSMENT CONTINUED

The Five Steps

▼ Look for the hazards

▼ Decide who might be harmed and how

▼ Evaluate the risks and decide whether precautions are adequate or more should be done

▼ Record your findings

▼ Review you assessment from time to time and revise it if necessary

---

WHETHER EXISTING MEASURES ARE ADEQUATE	WHAT MORE NEEDS TO BE DONE	DATE OF THE NEXT REVIEW

KEY REFERENCE: *5 Steps to risk assessment* **INDG163(rev1)**
(single copy free or priced packs of 10 ISBN 0 7176 1565 0)

WORKING IN AND MOVING AROUND THE WORKSHOP

About two thirds of all accidents in small engineering workshops happen during the movement of vehicles, people and goods. A safe, well-lit, clean workplace can help prevent many of these.

WORKPLACE (HEALTH, SAFETY AND WELFARE) REGULATIONS 1992 and APPROVED CODE OF PRACTICE *outlined*

A safe place of work

You must have:
- buildings in good repair
- precautions such as fences or rails to stop people or materials falling from open edges*
- space for safe movement and access, eg to machinery
- *safe glazing where necessary, marked to make it easy to see*
- floors, corridors and stairs free of obstruction
- good drainage at wet processes such as washing and cleaning
- windows that can be opened (if openable) and cleaned safely. *They should be designed to stop people falling out or bumping into them when open. You may need to fit anchor points if window cleaners have to use harnesses.*
- outdoor routes kept safe during icy conditions, eg salted/sanded and swept.

Safe movement

You must have:
- safe passage for pedestrians and vehicles - *you may need separate routes*
- level, even surfaces without holes or broken boards
- handrails on stairs *and ramps where necessary*
- safe doors, eg vision panels in swing doors
- surfaces which are not slippery
- *well lit outside areas.*

Workstations

Work stations and seating must fit the worker and the work. *Make sure that:*
- *back rests support the small of the back and foot rests are provided where necessary*
- *work surfaces are at a sensible height*
- *there is easy access to controls.*

Cleanliness

You must:
- provide clean floors and stairs, which are drained where necessary and not slippery
- provide clean premises, furniture and fittings
- provide containers for waste materials
- remove dust, refuse and trade-waste regularly
- clear up spillages promptly
- keep internal walls/ceilings clean. *They may need painting to help easy cleaning.*

---

*particularly on the flat roofs of offices provided in small industrial units, which are often used for storage; proper stairs should be provided for frequent access to these areas

MAINTENANCE

Maintaining the workshop and the equipment in it may pose different hazards from those encountered in the normal run of production work. Contractors as well as your own employees may be at increased risk, particularly during the repair and cleaning of plant containing toxic, flammable or hazardous materials, machinery and during work at heights or in confined spaces.

KEY REFERENCE: *Workplace health, safety and welfare* Approved Code of Practice and Guidance on Regulations   HSE Books ISBN 0 7176 0413 6

LIGHTING

Poor lighting is often a factor in accidents and can also increase visual fatigue.

THE LAW* ON LIGHTING outlined

You must provide:

■ good light - use natural light where possible but try to avoid glare

■ a good level of local lighting at work stations where necessary

■ suitable forms of lighting (fluorescent tubes operating at mains frequency may be dangerous with rotating machinery when the rotating part can appear to have stopped)

■ special fittings for flammable and explosive atmospheres, eg in spray booths, to reduce risks of ignition and explosion.

* Workplace Health, Safety and Welfare Regulation 1992

Problems	Typical activity	Average illuminance lux (lx) in work areas	Minimum measured illuminance (lx) at any point or a suitable place
General hazards from the movement of people, machines and vehicles in and around the workshop and visual fatigue from work requiring limited perception of detail	General work in the workshop, assembly of large components	100	50
Visual fatigue from work requiring perception of detail	Sheet metal work, general machining, office work	200	100
Visual fatigue from work requiring perception of fine detail	Drawing office work, assembly of electronic and other fine components	500	200

Avoid:

▼ large differences in the lighting of adjacent areas

▼ glare from direct sunlight by providing blinds, for example, and from directly visible lamps by excluding them sufficiently from lines of sight when necessary

▼ strobe effects by:

● supplying adjacent runs of light fittings from different phases

● providing a high frequency supply

● washing out the effect with local tungsten filament lighting

● if high intensity tungsten halogen or mercury lamps are used to provide local lighting, manufacturers' filters should always be kept in place.

For the electrical safety of lighting systems see pages 23-27.

KEY REFERENCE: *Lighting at work* HSG38 1997 HSE Books ISBN 0 7176 1232 5

GENERAL VENTILATION, TEMPERATURE AND TOILETS

Fans and/or additional air inlets (at low level) and outlets (at high level) may be needed in workshops where there are no means of ventilation other than air leaking in and out (particularly in units on some factory estates) and where:

- work generates hazardous airborne pollutants
- workshops have been sealed to conserve energy.

Provide **at least**
Five litres/second per occupant (eight is recommended for comfort) and air movement in the workshop of at least 0.1 to 0.15 metres/second.

Measure velocities, using specialist help if needed, at inlet ducts (to calculate air flows inwards) and inside the workshop (to calculate air movements).

THE LAW ON TEMPERATURE outlined

You must provide:
- a reasonable temperature and a thermometer inside workshops.

The temperature should be at least 16°C unless work involves severe physical effort, in which case the minimum should be 13°C.

THE LAW ON TOILETS AND WASHING FACILITIES outlined

You must provide:
- suitable and sufficient (and adequately ventilated and lit) sanitary conveniences and (nearby) washing facilities kept clean and orderly, *in the minimum numbers outlined below*
- separate rooms for men and women, except where they are for the use of one person and are capable of being secured from the inside
- hot and cold, or warm water with means of cleaning and drying.

No of people in workshop	No of WCs and wash stations
1-5	1
6-25	2
26-50	3
51-75	4
76-100	5

Alternatively, for sanitary accommodation used only by men, the following numbers are recommended:

No of men	No of WCs	No of urinals
1-15	1	1
16-30	2	1
31-45	2	2
46-60	3	2
61-75	3	3
76-90	4	4
91-100	4	4

Make separate calculations where groups such as office workers have separate accommodation.

KEY REFERENCE: Workplace Health, Safety and Welfare Regulations 1992
Approved Code of Practice and Guidance on Regulations L24   HSE Books ISBN 0 7176 0413 6

LIFTING EQUIPMENT

Although lifting, supporting and handling equipment can lighten the load of manual handling when properly used, many accidents happen when loads are dropped from lifting equipment, either because of poor slinging, or equipment failure or overloading.

Always:

▼ maintain all lifting equipment, including that used only occasionally, such as attachments to fork lift trucks

▼ train all users, particularly in the use of slings where necessary

▼ plan lifts in advance

▼ ensure that the weight and the distribution of any load is not beyond the capacity of the equipment being used

▼ provide safe places of work from which to maintain hoists and lifts, particularly at heights; do not allow overhead travelling cranes to work within 6 m of persons on crane tracks

▼ check the condition, type and size of any eyebolts used and ensure that the thread type matches the hole into which it is to be screwed.

THE LAW* ON LIFTING EQUIPMENT *outlined*

The same regulations now apply to all lifting equipment, which includes any equipment used at work for lifting or lowering loads, and lifting accessories such as chains, slings, eyebolts etc.

You should ensure that:

■ lifting equipment is sufficiently strong, stable and suitable for the proposed use, and marked to indicate its safe working load;

■ lifting equipment is positioned or installed to minimise the risk of injury, eg from the equipment or the load falling or striking people;

■ every part of a load (including, for example, pallets and stillages) and anything attached to the load and used in lifting (including for example the lifting points on skips) is of adequate strength;

■ lifting operations are planned, supervised and carried out in a safe manner by people who are competent;

■ lifting equipment (including accessories) is thoroughly examined for any defect before it is put into service for the first time (unless it is new and is covered by an EC declaration of conformity which is less than 12 months old). Where the safety of lifting equipment depends on installation conditions, it must be thoroughly examined after installation and before being put into use for the first time. Periodic thorough examinations are also required at six-monthly intervals for accessories and equipment used for lifting people, and at least annually for all other equipment; or at intervals laid down in an examination scheme drawn up by a competent person.

* Lifting Operations and Lifting Equipment Regulations 1998

KEY REFERENCE: *Safe use of lifting equipment: Lifting Operations and Lifting Equipment Regulations 1998* L113 HSE Books ISBN 0 7176 1628 2

MOVING GOODS SAFELY BY HAND

The unsafe movement of goods by hand, either by lifting or handling causes more accidents and ill health in small engineering workshops than any other single activity, especially to those most at risk, including the younger more inexperienced employees, the older and/or less physically fit, and those who may make an existing injury worse.

Back injuries are very common as are hand, arm, shoulder and neck injuries, particularly from unsafe, highly repetitive work. Cuts and abrasions from sharp edges are also very numerous.

MANUAL HANDLING OPERATIONS REGULATIONS 1992 *outlined*

Employers must:
■ avoid the need for hazardous manual lifting and handling if reasonably practicable
■ assess the risk of injury from any hazardous manual lifting and handling which cannot be avoided; and
■ reduce the risk of injury accordingly.

Employees must:
■ follow safe systems of work laid down by their employers
■ use mechanical aids provided by their employers properly
■ remember to use the training provided on lifting.

Sharp edges

These cause as many as a third of all accidents in some engineering workshops, resulting in cuts, abrasions, infected wounds, dermatitis, amputations and occasionally fractures.

Those working with sheet metal, either flat or coiled, heavy sharp items, such as tools and cutters, and scrap metal and swarf are most at risk.

Consider how to avoid handling sharp edges, and if this is not reasonably practicable, reduce exposure to them.

Reducing the risks

▼ Ask your supplier to remove or protect sharp edges, eg by machining out sharp edges or fitting plastic covers or padding.

▼ Remove sharp edges or protect them before handling.

▼ Avoid handling by using, for example, trays, jigs, holders or baskets.

▼ Minimise handling by automating processes by using, for example, conveyors, feed and discharge chutes.

▼ Store articles correctly so that they are retrieved easily.

Use personal protective equipment such as gloves, gauntlets and aprons, but only where these do not add to other risks from machinery, such as entanglement.

See Appendix 1 for checklists.

KEY REFERENCE: Manual Handling Operations Regulations 1992
Guidance on Regulations L23 1998 HSE Books ISBN 0 7176 2415 3

HOW TO LIFT SAFELY

Here are some important points, using a basic lifting operation as an example.

Plan the lift. Where is the load to be placed? Use appropriate handling aids if possible. Do you need help with the load? Remove obstructions such as discarded wrapping materials. For a long lift, such as floor-to-shoulder height, consider resting the load mid-way on a table or bench in order to change grip.

Position the feet

Feet apart, giving a balanced and stable base for lifting (tight skirts and unsuitable footwear make this difficult). Leading leg as far forward as is comfortable.

Adopt a good posture

When lifting from a low level, bend the knees. But do not kneel or overflex the knees. Keep the back straight (tucking in the chin helps).

Lean forward a little over the load if necessary to get a good grip. Keep the shoulders level and facing in the same direction as the hips.

Try to keep the arms within the boundary formed by the legs. The best position and type of grip depends on the circumstances and individual preference; but it must be secure. A hook grip is less tiring than keeping the fingers straight. If you need to vary the grip as the lift progresses, do it as smoothly as possible.

Keep close to the load

Keep the load close to the trunk for as long as possible. Keep the heaviest side of the load next to the trunk. If a close approach to the load is not possible, slide it towards you before trying to lift.

Lift smoothly, keeping control of the load.

Don't twist the trunk when turning to the side.

If precise positioning of the load is necessary, put it down first, then slide it into the desired position.

TRAINING FOR LIFTING AND HANDLING

This should cover:

▼ how to recognise harmful manual handling

▼ appropriate systems of work

▼ use of mechanical aids

▼ good handling technique.

(a) Plan the lift

(b) Determine the best lifting technique

(c) Get a secure grip

(d) Pull the load in close to your body

LIFTING AND HANDLING

Assessing risks

Assessment

Some of the important
questions to ask

Job

Job: Too high to
lift/lower?
Too rushed?
Too far to carry?
Too repetitive?
Too much twisting
involved?

Load: Too heavy?
Too large?
Too unstable?
Too hot/cold?
Too sharp?
Too difficult to
grasp?

Work area: Too dark?
Too slippery?
Too obstructed?
Too many steps?

Individual: Fit for the job?
In need of special
consideration or
training?

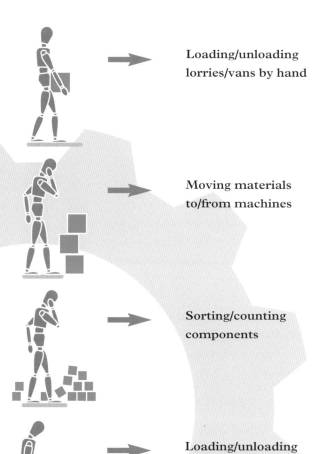

Loading/unloading
lorries/vans by hand

Moving materials
to/from machines

Sorting/counting
components

Loading/unloading
machines

Assembling and
packing

Preparing,
maintaining, moving
and repairing
machinery

Taking action

Short-term action	**Long-term solution**	

Provide help for heavy loads. Use the right person for the job → Palletise load(s). Use fork lift trucks

Break down loads into easily handled units/containers → Use conveyors/hoists/fork lift trucks

Use appropriate trained, fit, personnel → Ask suppliers to pre-sort before delivery. Weigh instead of count. Automate sorting

Raise stillages/bins to right height/position/ → Automate load/unload operations. Use hoists and/or mechanical aids

Use appropriate fit, trained, personnel at the right place. Rotate the work to prevent too much repetition → Provide good working environment, well lit and appropriate mechanical aids and tools to do the work without undue strain. 'Design out' the need for manual assembly and packing

Use appropriate fit, trained personnel → Provide unobstructed access and mechanical aids as necessary

ERGONOMIC MACHINE OPERATION, ASSEMBLY AND PACKING

TO MINIMISE RISKS

▼ avoid applying too much force for too long or too frequently using an awkward posture of the hand, wrist or arm.

CONSIDER

REDUCING THE FORCE INVOLVED
by, for example:

▼ keeping cutting tools sharp
▼ providing a larger gripping area
▼ supporting tools by means of balancers or tensioners (which may also help minimise vibration)

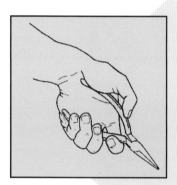 

A modified handle design can lead to a more comfortable hand position

REDUCING HIGHLY REPETITIVE MOVEMENTS by, for example:

▼ restructuring jobs so they contain more varied work
▼ automation

REDUCING THE NEED FOR AWKWARD POSTURES by, for example:

▼ changing the orientation of the part being worked upon to enable the wrist to be straight
▼ moving the operator so work is more comfortable

TRAINING IS VITAL, particularly:

▼ to prevent the repetition of old, bad ways of working
▼ to protect newer employees from working too quickly too soon

Most **ILL HEALTH** arises from:

▼ prolonged forceful or repetitive gripping, twisting, reaching or other movement without enough rest or recovery. This causes pain, a restriction of joint movement and soft tissue swelling, leading sometimes to permanent disability, mostly in the hands, arms and shoulders

▼ lifting and handling goods unsafely by hand.

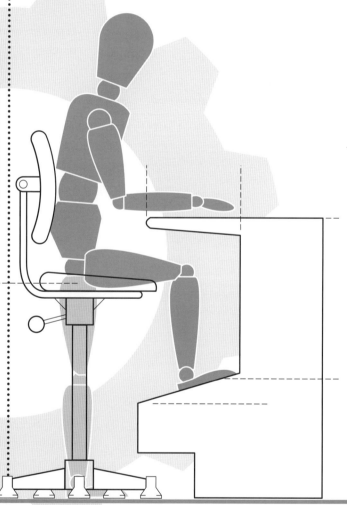

Consider workstations where both standing and sitting is possible. In general it is less physically stressful to sit, provided there are opportunities for moving around.

KEY REFERENCE: *Upper limb disorders in the workplace*
HSG60 HSE Books ISBN 0 7176 1978 8

ERGONOMIC ASPECTS TO CONSIDER

FOR OPERATING MACHINERY

▼ make frequently operated hand controls easy to reach and work

▼ if seats are provided leave sufficient room for knees and legs

▼ avoid bending and twisting to load/unload machines by having material/bins on racks which can be raised and lowered to keep them at waist height

▼ consider 'lean-on' or 'sit-stand', wheeled, sliding, suspended or fixed seats

▼ see page 76 for normal chairs.

FOR PROCESS OR ASSEMBLY WORK

▼ arrange the work in a semi-circle

▼ provide a swivel chair

▼ bring the work to the worker

▼ consider chairs with forward- tilting seats and backrests to help workers reach further without loss of support, and consider work surfaces and component trays which slope towards the worker

▼ racks for material and finished items should be adjustable so that work is comfortable to reach and put away.

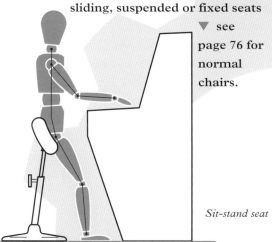

Sit-stand seat

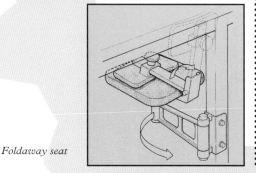

Foldaway seat

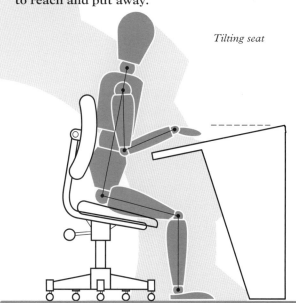

Tilting seat

FOR PRECISION WORK

▼ To avoid tense postures, a forward tilting seat and a work surface which slopes to the worker may be particularly helpful

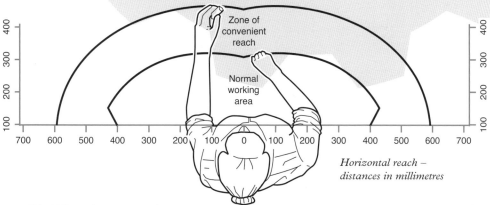

Zone of convenient reach

Normal working area

Horizontal reach – distances in millimetres

KEY REFERENCE: *Seating at work* HSG57 1997

HSE Books ISBN 0 7176 1231 7

MOVING VEHICLES SAFELY

Lorries, vans, cars and other vehicles and mobile plant are involved in many accidents, when reversing and manoeuvring in or around small workshops. These accidents cause injuries and occasionally deaths when victims are run over or crushed.

To reduce risks:

▼ Identify and clearly mark safe routes and locations for deliveries and despatches which are:

- away from pedestrians as much as possible
- in good condition
- well lit at all times when being used
- away from vulnerable plant
- marked clearly with suitably low speed limits.

▼ Provide loading bays with an exit from low level or a refuge to prevent crushing

▼ Do not allow untrained drivers to drive vehicles

▼ Avoid reversing (eg by suitable traffic routing for example) or provide help for reversing drivers if possible (eg a guide)

▼ Use speed bumps to limit traffic speeds where necessary and make sure there are gaps for any lift trucks which have to cross them

▼ Select and train your own drivers with care.

LOADING AND UNLOADING VEHICLES

Accidents frequently happen when people fall from vehicles. Avoid the need to climb on loads (by using curtains on the sides of vehicles or mechanical or proprietary sheeting systems), or provide safe access and safe systems of work. If it is necessary to walk on the top of high loads, safety lines and harnesses should be provided and worn.

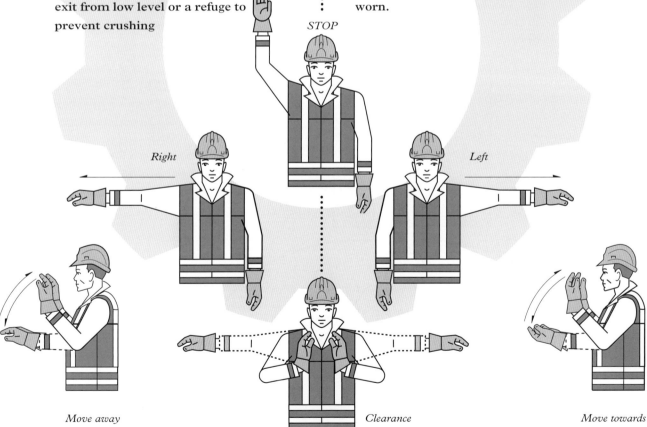

STOP

Right　*Left*

Move away　*Clearance*　*Move towards*

KEY REFERENCE: *Workplace transport safety* HSG136 HSE Books ISBN 0 7176 0935 9
Managing vehicle safety at the workplace INDG199 HSE Books (single copies free)

LIFT TRUCKS

HOW MOST ACCIDENTS HAPPEN

Lift trucks , (powered and non-powered, pedestrian and rider-operated,) are involved in many accidents in small engineering workshops. These are frequently caused by reversing unsafely, speeding, overloading, carrying passengers or lifting personnel the truck was not designed for, or drivers not being trained, and result in many serious injuries and some deaths every year when victims are run over or crushed.

Most **ILL HEALTH** arises from:
▼ using diesel trucks in enclosed confined working areas, leading to breathing problems
▼ poor seating and controls leading to back and upper limb disorders
▼ poor roadways which may cause vibration leading to back problems.

THE LAW* ON MOBILE WORK EQUIPMENT *outlined*

■ mobile work equipment includes fork lift trucks and any other work equipment which carries out work while it is travelling or which travels between different locations where it is used to carry out work.

■ where mobile work equipment is used for carrying people, it must be suitable for this purpose. Measures must be taken to reduce the risks to the safety of people being carried, the operator, and anyone else. These include measures to reduce the risks from equipment rolling over (most counter-balanced, seated centre-control fork lift trucks have a vertical mast which prevents them rolling more than 90º). Measures, such as fitting restraining systems, eg seat belts, must also be taken to reduce the risk of anyone being crushed between any part of the equipment and the ground if it rolls over or overturns.

■ you must ensure that self-propelled work equipment (ie work equipment which is propelled by its own motor mechanism) has appropriate facilities to ensure the safety of people in the workplace, including facilities for preventing its being started by an unauthorised person.

* *Provision and Use of Work Equipment Regulations 1998*

APPROVED CODE OF PRACTICE ON RIDER OPERATED LIFT TRUCKS - OPERATOR TRAINING *outlined*
■ *Employers to provide basic training by recognised instructors*
■ *Trainees to pass a test of their competence*
■ *Records to be kept of training.*

SAFE LIFT TRUCK OPERATION

■ Get the right truck for the job
■ Maintain all lift trucks regularly in accordance with the manufacturer's instructions, ensure seats are maintained to minimise unhealthy postures and vibration
■ Select only suitable personnel for training as operators/drivers, authorise operators/drivers in writing
■ Avoid routes near vulnerable plant, eg flammable liquid stores, or protect such plant
■ Segregate busy lift truck areas/routes from pedestrian and working areas as much as possible, pay particular attention to barriers, layout, visibility, lighting and warnings where lift trucks and people work alongside each other; enforce rules for low speed and safe reversing
■ Ensure operating surfaces are strong enough, well maintained and gradients are not too steep
■ Train all employees on lift truck movements, if the lift truck is used on the road (to load and unload, for example) provide a second person to help with traffic, as necessary
■ Rider operated lift trucks used regularly on the road for long periods, and their drivers, must be licensed by the Department of Transport
■ Keep keys secure when trucks not being used
■ Do not use forks, pallets or bins to lift persons to work at heights unless these are suitably modified; use properly designed mobile work platforms if possible.

KEY REFERENCE: *Rider operated lift trucks - operator training* L117 HSE Books ISBN 0 7176 2455 2; *Safety in working with lift trucks* HSE Books 2000 ISBN 07176 1781 5

CONTROLLING HAZARDOUS SUBSTANCES

Exposure to hazardous substances most frequently occurs when:

▼ machining (see page 30 for general control of hazardous substances and pages 36-37 for the control of metalworking fluids)
▼ welding (see page 63)
▼ painting (see page 69) and
▼ cleaning and degreasing (see page 60).

The control of dust, fume, spray and vapour- and the prevention of skin contact by adequate personal protection - will minimise risks of adverse health effects, but pay particular attention to precautions when **machining, welding, polishing** or **grinding**:

▼ nickel-copper and nickel-chrome alloys (found in coins, magnets, chemical and food process equipment and in the aerospace industry)
▼ stainless steel and nickel alloys; stainless steel and chromium alloys
▼ lead and lead alloys
▼ copper alloys containing beryllium (commonly found in the electrical industry and in high definition tools and dies - used, for example, in plastic injection moulding machines)
▼ cadmium-plated articles.

THE HEALTH AND SAFETY AT WORK ETC ACT 1974, SECTION 6 IN RELATION TO THE SUPPLY OF SUBSTANCES FOR USE AT WORK *outlined*

Suppliers must:
■ ensure so far as is reasonably practicable that the substance will be safe and without risks to health
■ provide adequate information about any risks to health or safety to which the inherent properties of the substance may give rise.

Labels and safety data sheets supplied with hazardous chemicals contain important information about hazards (see CHIP reference page 84) to help you use them safely.

The most common health effects from hazardous substances are:

▼ skin diseases such as dermatitis from metalworking fluids and oils
▼ lung problems, such as asthma, from isocyanate paints and glues
▼ poisonings, such as lead poisoning, and
▼ very rarely cancer, such as skin cancer from certain mineral oils.

THE CONTROL OF SUBSTANCES HAZARDOUS TO HEALTH REGULATIONS *outlined*

You must:
■ assess risks to health
■ prevent exposure, for example by using
   ● a less hazardous substance
   ● a different process
■ where prevention is not reasonably practicable, control exposure by, for example, isolating or enclosing the process or, if this is not reasonably practicable, local exhaust ventilation, and
■ where prevention or control is insufficient on its own, provide personal protective equipment
■ inform, instruct and train employees
■ carry out air monitoring and health surveillance where necessary.

A hazard may be defined as something that **can** cause harm - such as the chemicals in a tin of paint - while a risk may be seen as the chance of harm actually being done - which can vary with how the paint is actually used; spraying in an uncontrolled environment without personal protection could pose high levels of risk.

KEY REFERENCE: *Control of Substances Hazardous to Health Regulations 2002. Approved Code of Practice and guidance* L5 (Fourth edition) HSE Books 2002 ISBN 0 7176 2534 6

LOCAL EXHAUST VENTILATION (LEV)

SELECTION AND USE

LEV is a frequently used way of controlling exposure to hazardous substances by drawing them away from the breathing zones of workers into a hood and ductwork connected to an extract fan.

In many circumstances LEV may be cheaper and more effective than dilution ventilation. (Dilution ventilation works by introducing fresh air into the workplace to lower the general level of the hazardous substances in the air).

Heat losses from LEV may be minimised by heat recovery systems or recirculation of filtered air, but the latter only after specialist advice to prevent the recirculation of hazardous materials in harmful quantities.

> ### THE LAW★ ON MAINTENANCE, EXAMINATION AND TESTING OF LEV *outlined*
>
> In most small engineering workshops, employers must ensure that thorough examinations and tests are carried out:
>
> ■ every 14 months for most processes
> ■ every six months where metal articles are abraded or polished for more than 12 hours a week.
>
> Employers must also keep appropriate records for at least five years.
>
> *See Appendix 6 for details which should be recorded.*
>
> ★ *Control of Substances Hazardous to Health Regulations, regulation 9*

Someone with sufficient training, knowledge, skills and experience is required for the maintenance, examination and testing of LEV, and insurance companies frequently have the competence required.

To make the most of LEV

▼ Get an expert to design and install the most appropriate system, with the right hoods/enclosures, ductwork, air velocities and cleaning and filtration systems

  ▼ Keep the hood as close to the source of contamination as possible

  ▼ Make sure the fan draws air away from the operator

  ▼ Make sure partial enclosures are large enough to contain the work and that sprayers do not stand between the workpiece and point of extraction; consider a turntable for heavy items

LEV used to help draw welding fume from the breathing zone of a welder

LOCAL EXHAUST VENTILATION (LEV)

▼ Check and maintain the system, regularly particularly flexible ductwork

▼ Provide sufficient lighting (suitably protected) within the enclosure to encourage work to be done within the extracted area.

Common causes of LEV failure, which you can check easily and frequently yourself to keep it working properly include:

▼ physical damage to and poor positioning of hoods and booths

▼ damaged and/or blocked ductwork

▼ blocked, damaged, unsuitable or incorrectly installed filters

▼ too high/low water levels in wet collectors

▼ wear or corrosion of fan blades leading to build up of contaminant on blades

▼ slipping drive belts to fans

▼ poor lubrication of fan bearings.

It helps to keep a record of these checks.

Spraying in the direction of exhaust ventilation air movement; a turntable can help a sprayer avoid standing between the item being sprayed and the point of air extraction from the booth

KEY REFERENCE: *Introduction to local exhaust ventilation* HSG37
HSE Books ISBN 0 7176 1001 2

ELECTRICITY

HOW MOST ACCIDENTS HAPPEN

▼ Most accidents arise from contact with **live** conductors or equipment made **live** by faulty wiring and connections.

▼ Equipment using 240v AC may be as dangerous as that using 415v AC, depending on circumstances.

Each year, the use of electricity causes fatal and other injuries (eg burns) from electric shock and fire.

THE LAW★ ON 'LIVE' ELECTRICAL WORK
outlined

No electrical work should be carried out 'live' where there is a possibility of contact with a potentially dangerous live conductor unless:

■ it is **unreasonable** in all the circumstances for the equipment to be dead; and

■ it is **reasonable** in all the circumstances for the work to be carried out on or near it while it is live; and

■ suitable precautions (including, where necessary, suitable protective equipment) have been taken to prevent injury, such as proper work planning and the use of adequately trained and supervised staff.

★ See Key Reference

PRECAUTIONS necessary to prevent accidents require everyone in the workshop (including the self-employed) to use equipment safely and co-operate with the employer where necessary.

Employers in particular need to:

▼ develop a suitable system of maintenance for both fixed installations and portable equipment - advice from a competent person may be required

▼ ensure that electrical contractors are competent for the work they are expected to do; for example, are they registered with such organisations as the National Inspection Council for Electrical Installation Contracting or equivalent?

▼ select equipment which is suitable for the job (using reduced low-voltage equipment lowers the risk of serious injury)

▼ check that wiring and equipment is sound and properly installed, especially so that protection equipment such as fuse and switchgear will operate adequately in the case of faults. Universally accepted standards are described in BS 7671 *Requirements for electrical installations*

▼ ensure any electricians working for you are competent. Levels of qualification established by the Electrical Joint Industries Board may be of help here, but check that qualifications are relevant; a fully qualified TV technician may not be competent to re-wire a building.

KEY REFERENCES: *Memorandum of guidance on the Electricity at Work Regulations 1989* **HSR25 HSE Books ISBN 0 7176 1602 9;** *Electrical safety and you* **INDG231 (single copies free)**

PORTABLE ELECTRICAL EQUIPMENT

Use this list to check whether you are managing the risks from portable electrical equipment. Have you:

- prepared and implemented a system of maintenance for portable (and transportable) electrical equipment

- made sure that all items of portable electrical equipment are included in the maintenance system

- decided how to deal with 'unauthorised' equipment brought in by employees, eg portable, mains-operated radios

- collected information on where and how equipment is used. This information will help you decide what sort of checks/inspections/tests are required and at what frequencies

- provided straightforward training and information for all users (including yourself) to help them carry out user checks when equipment is used

- made sure that all equipment receives a formal visual inspection at appropriate intervals, carried out by someone who has been trained in what to look for

- considered preparing brief written guidance relating to visual inspection, what to look for, and procedures to follow when faults are found (and when unauthorised equipment is found)

- identified equipment which will need periodic combined inspection and testing

- established how often combined inspection and testing is appropriate (based on the type of equipment, how it is used, where it is used and the results of any previous checks/inspections/tests)

- appointed someone with the appropriate knowledge, training and experience to carry out the inspection and testing

- reviewed the results of checks/inspections/tests to identify any common trends and to confirm that the chosen inspection/test frequencies are appropriate

- made sure that the arrangements which you have made are being put into practice and that follow-up action is being taken?

REMEMBER THAT CHOOSING THE RIGHT EQUIPMENT AND CARRYING OUT VISUAL INSPECTIONS ARE PERHAPS THE MOST IMPORTANT WAYS TO MINIMISE THE RISKS.

ACTIVITY	PREFERRED EQUIPMENT
Work inside metal tanks which may be damp or humid (through condensation, for example)	Use pneumatic power tools. Lighting, if essential, should be 25V dc CTE* max and fixed out of reach.
‡Work on apparatus where water may be present (on a metalworking fluid circulation system on a machine tool) Work in close contact with metalwork in cool dry conditions	Use equipment operating at voltages of 50V ac, 120V dc or less. Higher-voltage equipment should be built to waterproof standard, eg BS EN 60529: 1992 *Specification for degrees of protection provided by enclosures*. The supply to earthed equipment should incorporate back-up protection which automatically disconnects the supply in the event of a fault, preferably earth monitoring.
Ad hoc maintenance work and outside work in good weather	Use equipment operating at voltages of 50v ac, 120v dc or less (110v ac CTE may be used in conjunction with all-insulated or double/insulated tools). Frequent cleaning of ventilation louvres is necesary.
	Reduced low-voltage equipment is preferred such as 110 volt CTE.

* CTE: *centre tapped to earth*

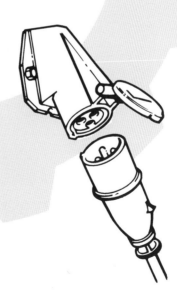

KEY REFERENCE: *Maintaining portable and transportable electrical equipment* HSG107 HSE Books ISBN 0 7176 0715 1

COMMON PROBLEMS WITH
FLEXIBLE LEADS, THEIR PLUGS AND SOCKETS
AND HOW TO AVOID THEM

Many accidents causing burn and shock injuries which are sometimes fatal
arise from poorly maintained and damaged leads, plugs and sockets.

PROBLEM	PRECAUTION
Failure to select the right equipment for the job/environment	Choose the right equipment. For example in a heavy fabrication shop, armoured, heat–, oil– and fire–resistant leads will often be necessary. Select reduced low voltage equipment (110V AC CTE max) whenever possible.
Failure to give adequate support to suspended cables (such as on pendant control leads for overhead cranes)	Use a wire or chain to relieve the cable of tension.
Poor joints in cables	**Replace** cables rather than repair them, particularly those used for a long time, or for short lengths when the cost of repair may be more than replacement; for longer lengths cut off the damaged part if it is close to an end or use a proprietary plug/ socket which provides both electrical and mechanical protection for cables. (If a coupler is used the socket must be on the supply side and the plug on the cable connected to the apparatus.)

Repairs should be carried out only by competent personnel; insulation and sheath damage can be repaired by vulcanising or using compatible proprietary self-sealing material together with a heat shrinkable plastic sleeve to give the finished joint necessary insulating value, strength and waterproofing. **Insulating tapes alone are unsatisfactory.** |
| Leads trailing too long may prevent circuit protection from operating within designed limits | Provide more convenient sockets, closer to work. |
| Cables and conductors insufficiently protected and liable to damage | Where liable to damage, for example in a busy area, re-route or provide a suitable cover, eg a conduit. |

PROBLEM	PRECAUTION
Cables and conductors too often flexed, which may cause damage to the insulating sheath or conductor	Check regularly, especially where the cable is terminated into the apparatus concerned, and repair or replace as necessary.
Damage to cables and conductors by portable equipment suchas soldering irons and portable grinders	Secure leads as far as possible out of harms way, where risk of damage is minimised.
Arcing when plugs withdrawn on load	Above 16A provide a switch (interlocked with plug if possible) to enable currents to be safely broken before withdrawing plug.
Weight and leverage of adaptors damaging socket outlets	Do not use adaptors or other plug–in devices where their weight and leverage may damage socket outlets. Provide sufficient socket outlets or, if necessary, use purpose made, portable multi–socket outlets.
Failure of plug cord grips	Ensure that it is the sheath which is being gripped not the conductors; do not remove plugs by pulling leads.
	Use the correct type of plug (particularly for armoured lead). Consider heavy-duty industrial plugs. Ensure it is terminated as per the manufacturer's instructions.
Loss of securing screws for plugs	Check them regularly, and replace missing ones.
Screened and armoured flexible cables incorrectly terminated in smaller portable equipment	Secure the whole cable using purpose-made glands/terminations fitted by a skilled person where necessary.
Overheated extension lead drums	Unwind lead from drum completely before use.

PRESSURISED PLANT AND SYSTEMS

THE LAW* ON PRESSURISED PLANT AND SYSTEMS *outlined*

- All plant and systems must be designed, constructed and installed to prevent danger
- Systems must be properly maintained
- Modifications or repairs must not cause danger
- There must be a written scheme for examination of certain pressure vessels, such as air receivers, steam boilers, fittings and pipework, drawn up by a competent person
- Examinations as set out in the written scheme must be carried out by a competent person
- Records must be kept in most cases

PRESSURE TESTING

▼ Accidents, some fatal, occur during pressure testing when the energy contained in the vessel under test is released with explosive force

▼ Wherever practicable, avoid using compressed air, steam or gas (which contains more than 200 times the energy of water of the same volume)

▼ Use hydraulic (liquid) pressure with suitable precautions and always, if possible, before leak testing (using air, steam or inert gas) components not intended as pressure vessels, eg vehicle fuel tanks, radiators, small castings, storage tanks and oil drums

INJECTION INJURIES

▼ Injuries, occasionally fatal, may be caused by accidental or deliberate injection of material and/or compressed air either through the skin or into a body orifice

▼ Ordinary working clothes do not significantly resist the penetration of compressed air into the body

▼ High-pressure fluid guns may inject material at 3-7000psi and cause serious injuries. Care should be taken to avoid accidental injections

▼ 'Horseplay' should be strictly forbidden

▼ Because the degree of injury may not always be immediately apparent, medical advice should always be sought after compressed air penetration occurs or is suspected.

KEY REFERENCE: *Safety of pressure systems. Pressure Systems Safety Regulations 2000. Approved Code of Practice HSE Books ISBN 0 7176 1767 X
Compressed air safety HSG39 HSE Books ISBN 0 7176 1531 6

MACHINING

HOW MOST ACCIDENTS HAPPEN

Most accidents at all types of machine, including automatic and CNC machines, happen to **operators** during normal operation when:

▼ loading/unloading components

▼ removing swarf

▼ taking measurements and making adjustments (to the coolant supply in particular).

On manually operated machines, the most dangerous machine movements are the rotating, cutting, shearing, sawing or pressing movements of tools, particularly on:

▼ presses

▼ drilling machines

▼ milling machines

▼ lathes

▼ metal cutting saws

▼ guillotines and

▼ grinding machines.

Hands are most frequently injured, the most numerous injuries being cuts and abrasions, many of which are severe. Broken bones and dislocations are numerous. Amputations of fingers and hands are not infrequent and there are some fatalities, often arising from entanglements, every year. Eye injuries are also common.

On automatic and computer controlled machinery, a larger proportion of accidents happens at automatically and computer controlled clamps, axes, tables, swarf removal equipment, chucks and other work handling equipment.

At all types of machinery a large number of accidents happen to setters, electricians and maintenance personnel during set-up, inspection, fault-finding, maintenance and repair.

Most **ILL HEALTH** arises from:

▼ unsafe loading/unloading and handling of components, in particular when highly repetitive, which may cause back injuries and upper limb disorders

▼ skin contact with metalworking fluids, for example when preparing fluids or handling components, which may cause skin irritation and dermatitis

▼ breathing in aerosols, oil mists and fumes from metalworking fluids during machining which may cause irritation of the eyes, nose and throat, and occasionally breathing difficulties such as bronchitis and asthma

▼ sharp edges and swarf which may cause cuts which exacerbate dermatitis

▼ high noise levels which may cause deafness most frequently at machines which generate impacts when operating, higher speed machines or groups of machines running together

▼ vibration, particularly when grinding.

MACHINING
GOOD PRACTICE

SAFETY MEASURES

▼ To prevent access to dangerous movements during batch production at manually operated machines use fixed guards with:

- jigs and fixtures (such as sliding trays) to load and unload components away from the tools
- safe means of removing swarf (such as a hook or rake which may be inserted through small openings in fixed guards) and adjusting coolant (such as taps outside fixed guards).

▼ Use fixed and interlocking guards or safety devices providing equivalent protection at automatic and CNC machines to ensure all dangerous movements, not only tools, are guarded (see page 32 and individual machines for further guidance on guarding CNC machines).

▼ Control noise by engineering means at source or adapt and extend guards to serve as noise enclosures (eg by lining them with noise absorbent materials). (See pages 40-42).

▼ Use guards to help enclose and control hazardous substances with LEV where appropriate.

▼ Manually operated machines used infrequently for one-off operations such as those often found in toolrooms may require constant adjustment and close observation; guards may also need to be readily adjustable and allow close observation.

TRAINING ESSENTIALS

Operators should know:

▼ what the main dangers are, how the main safeguards work and who should be notified of defective ones

▼ how to start, operate and stop the machine safely

▼ what to wear (eg protective equipment) and what not to wear (eg loose clothing at some machines)

▼ how to
- load and unload components
- remove swarf, and
- adjust coolant flow safely

▼ not to clean machines using compressed air to blow material away - industrial vacuum cleaners or brushes should be used

▼ how to work safely with any metalworking fluids used.

Maintenance and setting personnel should know:

▼ that before inspection, cleaning, maintenance and repair, machines must in general be switched off and isolated

▼ where power is necessary, how to work safely, for example by using:
- written systems of work
- permits to work on complex or hazardous plant, and
- warning signs

▼ how to maintain metalworking fluids to minimise health risks.

THE PROVISION AND USE OF WORK EQUIPMENT REGULATIONS 1998 *outlined* (equipment includes machinery)

Employers and others must ensure that:

■ suitable equipment is provided for the jobs involved

■ information and instruction are adequate

■ equipment is maintained in good working order and repair

■ training is provided for operators and supervisors

■ equipment is safeguarded to prevent risks from mechanical and other specific hazards

■ equipment is provided with appropriate and effective controls

■ maintenance is carried out safely

■ some work equipment is subject to inspection to ensure that is safe to use (see page 31).

The Regulations also contain requirements relating to mobile work equipment (see page 19) and power presses (see page 48).

KEY REFERENCE: *Provision and Use of Work Equipment Regulations 1998*
ACOP and Guidance on Regulations **L22 HSE Books ISBN 0 7176 1626 6**

MACHINING

The Provision and Use of Work Equipment Regulations 1998 impose requirements relating not just to preventing access to dangerous parts of machinery, but also to the following:

▼ information and instruction
▼ inspection
▼ safe maintenance operations
▼ starting and stopping machines safely (including emergency stops)
▼ control systems
▼ means of isolating work equipment from sources of energy
▼ stability
▼ lighting
▼ markings
▼ warning devices.

You will need to carry out risk assessments on your existing machinery in order to identify whether it complies with all of the requirements. You can use the risk assessment proforma in Appendix 3 to help.

INSPECTION OF WORK EQUIPMENT

Inspection of work equipment should be carried out where a significant risk of injury (one which could foreseeably result in a major injury or worse) may result from:

▼ incorrect installation or reinstallation of the equipment
▼ deterioration of the work equipment leading to danger, or
▼ as a result of exceptional circumstances which could affect the safe operation of the work equipment (for example, if it is damaged).

Inspection will be necessary when equipment or parts of equipment deteriorate and lead to danger and where this will not be adequately controlled through operator checks and normal servicing regimes. It will not therefore apply to everyday risks at work equipment, which can be detected and rectified during routine operator checks and maintenance.

The purpose of an inspection is to identify whether the equipment can be operated, adjusted or maintained safely and that any deterioration (such as damage or wear) can be detected and remedied before it results in unacceptable risks.

Inspections should include visual and functional checks of the equipment, and sometimes testing. This will depend on the complexity of the equipment, on where and how it is used, and on what the risks to health or safety could be if the equipment is operated in an unsafe condition.

A risk assessment should be carried out to determine whether an inspection is necessary and, if so, what form it should take. The assessment should also state the intervals at which inspections should be carried out. Records of the assessment and the inspections should be kept.

Some examples of equipment which is likely to be subject to inspection:

■ *Hydraulic presses and press brakes*
■ *Non-lifting parts of fork lift trucks*
■ *Die-casting machines*

BUYING AND SELLING MACHINERY

NEW*

A **buyer** of 'new' machinery should look for the 'CE' mark, which should indicate:

▼ the supplier's claim to conformity with the Supply of Machinery (Safety) Regulations, which implements the Machinery Directive in the UK

▼ the machinery meets essential health and safety requirements to eliminate risks of injury from most sources

▼ there should be little if anything further to do to make the machinery safe if 'Instructions for use' are followed.

If you buy a machine with a CE mark, assess that it is safe and without risks to health by, for example, checking it against the standards on any similar machines you may already have; it should at least meet current standards. You can use the risk assessment proforma in Appendix 3 to help check the machine.

An outline of what is defined as 'machinery' from the
SUPPLY OF MACHINERY (SAFETY) REGULATIONS

■ An assembly of linked parts or components, at least one of which moves including the appropriate actuators, control and power circuits, joined together for a specific application, in particular for the processing, treatment, moving or packaging of a material

■ An assembly of machines which, in order to achieve the same end, are arranged and controlled so that they function as an integral whole

■ Interchangeable equipment modifying the function of a machine which is supplied for the purpose of being assembled with an item of machinery by the operator himself save for any equipment which is a spare part or tool

■ A 'safety component' placed on the market separately from machinery to fulfill a safety function when in use and the failure or malfunction of which endangers safety or health.

For a **seller** of 'new' machinery the 'CE' mark among other things should be a claim for the most commonly used machine tools in engineering that at least:

▼ hazards, where reasonably practicable, have been designed out

▼ mechanical dangers are safeguarded with guards and safety devices fitted and working together with clear instructions provided on how risks not safeguarded are to be avoided

▼ the machine is as quiet as is reasonably practicable with noise reduced at source or enclosed (the noise emission level must be stated in 'Information for use')

▼ steps have been taken to control emissions of harmful substances when the machine is working by, for example, containment or by providing for connection to extraction equipment

▼ instructions for use are provided to indicate clearly in English how the machine may be safely installed, operated, maintained, removed or dismantled; where it is not immediately clear how safeguards work as on some computer controlled machinery clear information should be provided on:
  ● how they work
  ● how they may be checked
  ● how to maintain them, and
  ● what to do in case of faults/failures

▼ information on vibration is provided and vibration minimised for hand-held machines

▼ metalworking fluids can be cooled where necessary, delivered and removed safely with risks of contamination minimised, eg from filter blockages or high working temperatures; information for use should specify how to use fluids safely at the machine.

$C \in$

*'New' means new to the European Union. An old, second-hand machine from the Far East or Eastern Europe, for example, is regarded as 'new' to the European Union for the purposes of the Supply of Machinery (Safety) Regulations 1992. Carrying out substantial refurbishment, such as fitting a CNC control to a previously manual machine, may also result in a 'new' machine subject to these Regulations.

BUYING AND SELLING MACHINERY

SUPPLY OF MACHINERY (SAFETY) REGULATIONS 1992 AND AMENDMENT REGULATIONS 1994 *outlined*

If you are a responsible person for the supply of new machinery or, from outside the EU, new or secondhand machinery for the first time:

■ AS A COMPLETE MACHINE (such as a lathe)

■ AS INTERCHANGEABLE EQUIPMENT TO MODIFY THE FUNCTION OF ANOTHER MACHINE (such as an internal grinding attachment for a centre lathe)
  ● make sure it complies with essential health and safety requirements (of the Machinery Directive, listed in the Supply of Machinery (Safety) Regulations)
  ● keep relevant information on its design, construction and use so that a 'technical file' (or part of one) may be assembled if an enforcing authority asks for it
  ● provide 'Instructions for use' in the language of the country where it will be used
  ● issue a Declaration of Conformity to your customer
  ● attach the 'CE' mark
  ● ensure that it is safe

■ AS A SAFETY COMPONENT
  ● take all the above steps but do not attach the 'CE' mark

■ AS PART OF ANOTHER MACHINE, which cannot function independently, (eg a swarf conveyor intended for incorporation into another machine)
  ● take all the above steps and issue a Declaration of Incorporation instead of Conformity to your customer, in which case *do not* attach the 'CE' mark

■ SPECIAL REQUIREMENTS apply to presses and other highly dangerous machines and some safety components, which must either conform to the BS EN 'C' standard or have EC-type examination.

SECOND-HAND

Sellers of second-hand machinery from outside the European Union must comply with the law on **new** machinery.

Refurbished machinery from inside the European Union may also be 'new' within the meaning of the law, and have to comply. The degree of refurbishment will decide whether the machinery is 'new' or not. A substantial refurbishment which gives machinery new functions, such as computer control, which it didn't have before, is likely to make the machinery 'new'. A new coat of paint and the straight replacement of worn-out items, on the other hand, most likely would not.

Consult your local HSE inspector where it is not clear.

Buyers of second-hand machinery should make sure that it complies with the requirements of the Provision and Use of Work Equipment Regulations 1998 (see page 30-33). The risk assessment proforma in Appendix 3 can be used to help check compliance.

THE HEALTH AND SAFETY AT WORK ETC ACT 1974 SECTION 6, *on the supply of machinery, new or old, from whatever source, outlined*

It must be:
■ so far as is reasonably practicable designed and constructed so that it is safe and without risks to health
■ accompanied by adequate information for use.

Only a written undertaking from the buyer that **specified** steps will be taken to safeguard the machine he/she is buying relieves the supplier of his duties in relation to second-hand machines from within the EU.

KEY REFERENCES: *Product standards: Machinery* DTI (tel: 0870 150 2500) *Supplying new machinery* INDG270, *Buying new machinery* INDG271 HSE Books

METALWORKING FLUIDS

Correctly managing your metalworking fluids will reduce the risk of ill health, prolong the life of the fluid, increase tool life, and improve the machining performance.

ILL HEALTH from metalworking fluids, used neat or mixed with water, most commonly arises from:

a) **skin contact** during

▼ preparation, application and removal of fluid
▼ handling of workpieces
▼ splashing when machining
▼ changing and setting of tools
▼ maintainance and cleaning of machines

causing skin irritation and dermatitis, and

b) **breathing in** aerosols, mist and fumes when machining causing irritation of the eyes, nose and throat and occasionally breathing difficulties such as bronchitis and asthma.

As most metalworking fluids, either as concentrates or when in use, are or contain hazardous substances, the strategy for controlling them outlined on page 20 is almost always relevant and useful.

In particular:

▼ maintain them in good condition (see next page)
▼ operate and maintain processes to minimise mist, fume, vapour and splashing

▼ make suitable arrangements to clean contaminated overalls and clothing
▼ do not use unrefined mineral oils and mildly refined distilled oils which may cause cancer and for which safer alternatives are available.

Cases of oil acne (folliculitis - irritation of the hair roots from prolonged and regular contact with neat oils) and skin cancer must be reported to HSE (see page 79).

Where there is significant skin contact or exposure to fume, mists or aerosols, health surveillance is likely to be needed.

Appoint a responsible person to:

▼ encourage high standards of personal hygiene
▼ undertake regular skin inspections (about once a month)
▼ check that controls are effective
▼ encourage employees to complete questionnaires (about once a year) for both skin and breathing symptoms
▼ review absence records
▼ advise those with problems to seek further medical advice.

Appendix 2 (pages 99-100) gives examples of useful questionnaires.

KEY REFERENCE: *Working safely with metalworking fluids* (pack)
HSE Books ISBN 0 7176 2561 3

SAFE WORKING WITH METALWORKING FLUIDS
MINIMISE RISKS BY

MAINTAINING FLUIDS IN GOOD CONDITION

DO:
- read and follow supplier's guidance
- use fluids compatible with machines, eg those that will not:
  - strip paint from the machine to block filters, or
  - dissolve metals being worked such as cobalt, chromium and nickel which may cause health problems later if inhaled or in contact with skin
- make use of special expertise, and develop in-house competence to maintain fluids by, for example, keeping a weekly record of:
  - visual sump inspections for fluid and tramp oil leaks
  - concentration and pH measurements, and
  - bacteria dip slide measurements
- top up in accordance with suppliers instructions
- keep machines clean and free from debris
- clean sumps, pipework and machines before refilling with fluids which should be recently mixed outside the machine in clean containers adding concentrate to drinking quality water
- use a refractometer to check strengths.

DON'T:
- store fluids outside, where strong sunlight or frost may damage water-mix fluids and moisture may lead to the contamination of neat oils
- add too much biocide which will increase the risks of skin sensitisation and respiratory irritation
- use fluids beyond their normal working life
- allow other oils used to lubricate the machine to contaminate metalworking fluid.

OPERATING MACHINES SAFELY

DO:
- train and instruct employees in the hazards and safeguards
- enclose sources of emissions and aerosols
- maintain fluid flow at correct volumes and pressures, as:
  - insufficient flow will lead to higher working temperatures and more fume
  - higher pressures may lead to more mist formation
  - larger volumes may increase risks of splashing
- provide local exhaust ventilation at machines to remove fume and mist at harmful levels and have the ventilation system examined and tested by a competent person every 14 months.

DON'T:
- allow fluids to overheat as this increases risks of biological contamination
- allow water-mix fluids to stagnate when not in use (for example, use small circulation pumps or pass air gently through the fluid)
- use air lines to blow components clean - use a vacuum-type cleaner instead.

MAINTAINING HIGH STANDARDS OF PERSONAL HYGIENE

DO:
- use machines, enclosures and extraction equipment properly to minimise splashing and breathing aerosols and mists
- wash with soap and water regularly to remove metalworking fluids
- use an after-work cream each time after washing and drying
- wear clean overalls and keep oily rags out of pockets
- cover cuts and abrasions with waterproof dressings.

DON'T:
- wear jewellery, rings or watch straps under which fluids may collect and be difficult to clean
- eat, drink or smoke in working areas.

KEY REFERENCE: *Working with metalworking fluids* INDG365 HSE Books (single copies free; ISBN 0 7176 2545 1 for priced packs of 10)

NOISE

Too much loud noise damages hearing by causing:

▼ deafness, or

▼ permanent tinnitus (ringing in the ear).

If you cannot hear clearly what someone is saying (in a normal voice) 2 m away, the noise level is likely to be 85dB(A) or higher:

TYPICAL MINIMUM NOISE LEVELS NEXT TO OPERATIONS WHERE NO STEPS HAVE BEEN TAKEN TO REDUCE NOISE:

	dB(A)
air exhausting from pneumatic equipment	85-95
grinding on pedestal grinder	90-95
discharging metal objects into metal tins/chutes	85-95
general noise level in fabrication shop	85-95
using vibratory bowl feeders	90-100
hammering steel	95-100
guillotining	95-100
multi-spindle automatic turning	95-105
circular sawing - metal	95-105
pressing - blanking	95-110
- punch pressing	110-120
riveting	100-110

Actual noise levels can be higher than those shown above.

MEASURING NOISE

Exposure to noise is measured in decibels - usually written as dB(A). The noise level (loudness) is measured as a scale from a silent zero dB(A) to 140dB(A) for the noisiest situations. For most jobs risk depends not only on noise levels but how long people are exposed to them. The total amount of noise exposure over the whole working day is called the daily personal noise exposure (usually shortened to $L_{EP,d}$).

Many engineering workshops may need to have their noise levels measured. This should be done by people who understand and can apply HSE's guidance on how to measure noise.

KEY REFERENCE: *Reducing noise at work: Guidance on the Noise at Work Regulations 1989* L108 ISBN 0 7176 1511 1; HSE website: www.hse.gov.uk/noise

NOISE

NOISE AT WORK REGULATIONS 1989 *outlined*

Action to be taken where $L_{EP,d}$ is likely to be

	85dB(A)	90dB(A)
Employers must:		
■ reduce risk of hearing damage to lowest level reasonably practicable	★	★
■ have noise assessed by a competent person	★	★
■ keep records of assessment until a new one is made	★	★
■ reduce exposure to noise as far as is reasonably practicable by means other than ear protectors		★
■ provide information, instruction and training to employees	★	★
■ mark ear protection zones with notices, as far as is reasonably practicable		★
■ ensure so far as is practicable that ear protectors are:		
● provided to all who ask for them	★	
● provided to all exposed		★
● maintained and repaired	★	★
● used by all exposed		★
■ ensure so far as is reasonably practicable that all who go into marked ear protection zones use ear protectors		★
■ ensure that all equipment issued under the Regulations is used and maintained.	★	★
Employees must, so far as is practicable:		
■ use ear protectors		★
■ use any other protective equipment	★	★
■ report any defects.	★	★

A new European Directive dealing with noise has been agreed. It is expected that new noise at work legislation will come into force in 2006, when the above action levels will be reduced.

THE LAW* ON NOISE ASSESSMENTS *outlined*

Noise assessments must:

■ identify persons at risk
■ enable employers to:
  ● reduce noise where reasonably practicable other than by the provision of ear protection
  ● provide the right sort of ear protection
  ● establish the correct protection zones
  ● give suitable information to employees
■ be reviewed when circumstances change.

* Noise at Work Regulations 1989

Regular hearing checks (health surveillance) may be required under the Management of Health and Safety at Work Regulations 1992 (see page 1) depending on how noisy the workshop is. It is good practice to carry out hearing checks on all employees whose daily personal noise exposure regularly equals or exceeds 90dB(A).

You should take noise risks into account when buying new work equipment. Make sure that you get proper information about the levels of noise likely to be produced by the equipment. Consider a policy of purchasing only low-noise equipment.

KEY REFERENCE: *Noise at Work: Advice for employers*
INDG362 HSE Books (single copies free; ISBN 0 7176 2539 7 for priced packs of 10)

HOW TO MAKE THE MOST OF NOISE ASSESSMENTS

TASK 1	TASK 2	TASK 3
Operating a power press carrying out a blanking operation	Sorting metal components into metal bins, around workshop	Breaks taken at/near machines
Sample Leq* dB(A) 98 for 3 hours giving fractional exposure **'f' value 2.37**	**Sample Leq dB(A)** 93 for 4 hours giving fractional exposure **'f' value 1.00**	**Sample Leq dB(A)** 88 for 1 hour giving fractional exposure **'f' value 0.08**

Total 'f' = 3.45 Assessed LEP,d = 95 dB(A)

REDUCE NOISE

Use protective measures as for Task 2 until tools designed to use shear/skew cut and/or feed automated and/or discharge chutes/bins lined with noise absorbent material and/or press enclosed, to give **85dB(A)**. Maintain noise reduction measures. Make ear protection available. Provide information, instruction, training.	Line metal bins with noise absorbent materials, to give **90-91 dB(A)**. Mark ear protection zones. Provide and maintain ear protectors and warning signs. Make sure protectors are worn. Provide information, instruction, training. Review when circumstances change.	Provide quiet rest/break room, to give **<85 dB(A)**.

For most industrial situations LEP,d can be calculated using Figure 2 from the key reference below.

*(Leq is a continuous equivalent sound level)

KEY REFERENCE: *Reducing noise at work: Guidance on the Noise at Work Regulations 1989* L108 ISBN 0 7176 1511 1; HSE website: www.hse.gov.uk/noise

HOW TO REDUCE NOISE

Noise may be reduced by:

▼ eliminating the need for the process concerned, all of the time...

...or part of the time by substituting a quieter machine or process

▼ by changing the way an operation is carried out, or a machine works

▼ by maintaining machinery

▼ by enclosing the machine or process in enclosures...

...or in separate areas/rooms

▼ by using noise absorbent material near noisy operations.

Examples of successful noise reduction

▼ increasing precision in castings, more accurate metal cutting (eg by laser, by maintaining guillotine blades) may reduce the need to trim, grind or chip excess material

▼ operating an air ejector on a press only for the time required to eject the component

▼ welding instead of riveting

▼ using quieter riveting machines

▼ using a mechanical instead of pneumatic ejector on a press

▼ applying a shear edge to press tools for blanking

▼ using only sufficient air pressure to operate the machine reliably

▼ avoiding or cushioning impacts between noisy parts by, for example, using rubber conveyors or chutes and bins lined with rubber or plastic

▼ by providing effective means of vibration isolation

▼ damping vibrating surfaces to reduce the tendency of metal surfaces to ring by using surface coatings or plates, as on metal cutting circular saw blades

▼ using silencers to reduce noise caused by turbulence at air exhausts and jets

▼ using tie bars on C-frame presses where provided

▼ lubricating moving parts as appropriate

▼ fitting noise absorbent panels as for example around cold heading machines, power and punch presses

▼ fitting noise absorbent room dividers such as plastic curtains to separate noisy from quiet operations

▼ fitting suspended noise absorbers in a fabrication workshop to lower high intermittent noise levels.

KEY REFERENCE: *Reducing noise at work: Guidance on the Noise at Work Regulations 1989* L108 ISBN 0 7176 1511 1; HSE website: www.hse.gov.uk/noise

ENGINEERING CONTROL

In many circumstances engineering control may be the most cost effective way of reducing noise. Expert analysis of noise sources, and identification of the right control measures are necessary.

Engineering control has been effective in many ways. For example:

Operation	Method	Reduction
vibratory feeders, and conveyors	damping high frequency vibration without affecting performance	95 dB(A) Leq to 73 dB(A) Leq
hydraulic power packs for guillotines	mounting the motor pump unit on a rigid frame, isolating it and the valve bank from the machine body	96 dB(A) Leq to 79 dB(A) Leq
machining of castings	reducing the vibration of the casting by using a pair of damping straps	104 dB(A) Leq to 88 dB(A) Leq
blanking	introducing small amounts of stagger and shear into the press tools	98 dB(A) Leq to 91 dB(A) Leq
blanking	isolation of the press frame from its fabricated legs using 6 mm composite pads	101 dB(A) Leq to 92 dB(A) Leq
blanking	fitting dynamic vibration absorbers to the flywheel from which 'bell-like' tones radiated	99 dB(A) Leq to 89 dB(A) Leq

TRAINING SPECIFICS

Training for those who work in noisy areas should include:
- what the risk is to their hearing
- how to use any noise enclosure provided
- who to report defective enclosures to
- how to follow systems of work designed to reduce exposure
- when and how to use ear protectors provided, who to report defective ones to, and how to keep them clean
- that hearing problems must be reported to a doctor, with details of the noise involved.

KEY REFERENCE: *Sound solutions* HSG138 HSE Books ISBN 0 7176 0791 7
Protect your hearing or lose it INDG362 2002 (single copy free; ISBN 0 7176 2539 7 for priced packs of 10 copies) HSE Books

VIBRATION

Vibration White Finger (VWF), known as 'dead finger' or 'dead hand', is widespread in some workshops and is the most obvious symptom of hand-arm vibration syndrome (HAVS);

▼ Attacks are painful and can result in the loss of sense of touch and of the ability to grip properly

▼ The most common causes are work with:

- hammers and chisels
- powered percussive metalworking tools including hammers for riveting, clinching and flanging
- tagging machines to shape bar material
- pedestal and hand-held grinding and polishing machines

although any regular prolonged use of any high-vibration tool or machine which causes tingling or numbness after five to ten minutes is a possible cause.

Personal protective equipment will not normally reduce the amount of vibration reaching the worker's hands.

THE LAW ON VIBRATION *outlined*

Unlike noise there are currently no specific regulations dealing with vibration, but where the hazard exists the Management of Health and Safety at Work Regulations (see page 1) and Provision and Use of Work Equipment Regulations (see page 30) apply. However, a European Directive which deals with hand-arm vibration risks has been agreed and will result in UK Regulations in 2005.

TO MINIMISE HARM

▼ Identify hazardous jobs

▼ Consider changing the process or product design to eliminate or reduce the use of vibrating machinery

For example:
- Mechanise or automate
- Use hydraulic rather than pneumatic impulsive riveting
- Rough machine rather than hand grind

▼ Choose low vibration equipment such as:

- properly balanced grinding wheels, rotary rather than impact or impulse action-powered screwdrivers, nut runners and torque wrenches for assembly work, and low-vibration or recoilless chipping hammers or machines incorporating vibration reducing features such as isolating handles

▼ Maintain equipment properly by keeping cutting tools sharp, dressing grinding wheels properly, and replacing anti vibration mounts to maintain their effectiveness

▼ Reduce the amount of hand force needed when grinding, for example, by supporting heavy workpieces and using jigs with anti-vibration mounts

▼ Carry out health surveillance of exposed workers under the general supervision of a medical practitioner, and

▼ Have symptoms investigated further by someone able to assess them medically

▼ Ensure that heating is adequate to keep hands and body warm.

KEY REFERENCES: *Hand-arm vibration* HSG88 HSE Books ISBN 0 7176 0743 7
Vibration solutions HSG170 HSE Books ISBN 0 7176 0954 5
Power tools: How to reduce vibration health risks INDG338 (single copies free;
ISBN 0 7176 2008 5 for priced packs of 15); HSE website: www.hse.gov.uk/vibration

MILLING AND MACHINING CENTRE WORK

HOW MOST ACCIDENTS HAPPEN

▼ Entanglement and contact with rotating cutters when:
- loading/unloading components
- removing swarf
- measuring
- adjusting coolant flow.

These cause entanglement injuries such as broken bones, and dislocations, amputations and lacerations

▼ not wearing eye protection when machining, cleaning and removing swarf.

Most **ILL HEALTH** arises from:

▼ unsafe handling (see pages 12-17), harmful metalworking fluids (see pages 36-37), and too much noise (see pages 38-42), but in particular

▼ handling heavier workpieces at larger machines which may require mechanical aids such as hoists

▼ noise (which may be difficult to predict and reduce at source) from cutters operating against workpieces.

TRAINING SPECIFICS

As well as understanding general rules for the safe operation of machinery (see page 30), operators need to know how to:
- remove swarf
- adjust coolant flow
- load and unload components safely.

KEY SAFETY MEASURES

For a manual horizontal milling machine used for a variety of workpieces:
- Fixed guard adjustable by means of a tool
- False table to help restrict access to cutter.

KEY REFERENCES: BS EN 13128: 2001 *Machine tools - Safety - Milling machines (including boring machines);* **BS EN 12417: 2001** *Machine tools - Safety - Machining centres*

MILLING MACHINE AND MACHINING CENTRE WORK

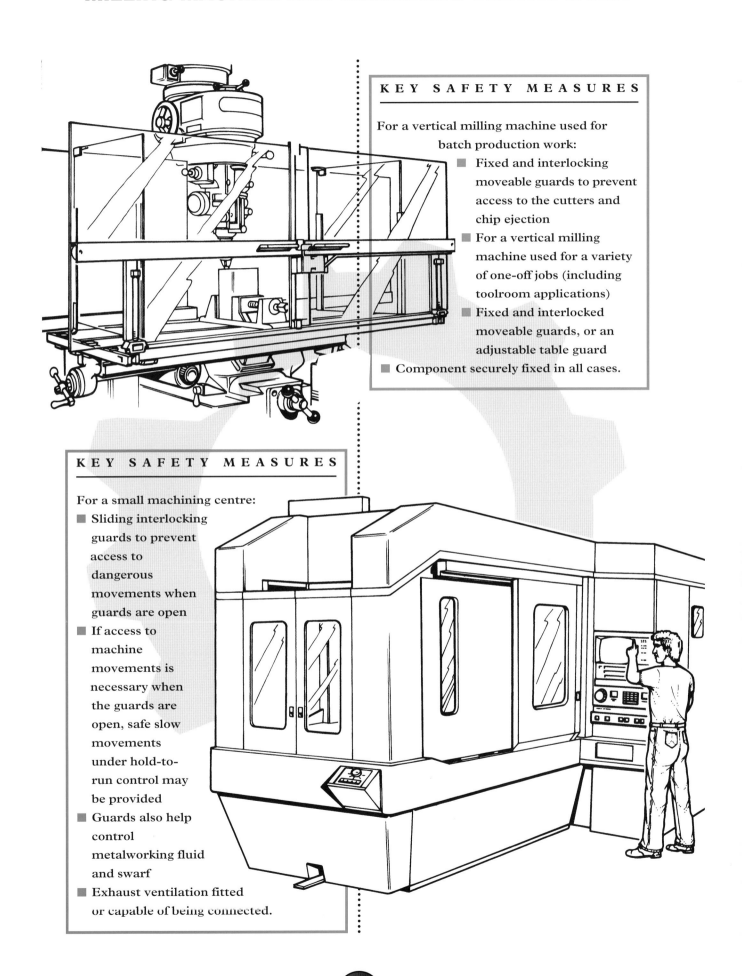

KEY SAFETY MEASURES

For a vertical milling machine used for batch production work:

- Fixed and interlocking moveable guards to prevent access to the cutters and chip ejection
- For a vertical milling machine used for a variety of one-off jobs (including toolroom applications)
- Fixed and interlocked moveable guards, or an adjustable table guard
- Component securely fixed in all cases.

KEY SAFETY MEASURES

For a small machining centre:

- Sliding interlocking guards to prevent access to dangerous movements when guards are open
- If access to machine movements is necessary when the guards are open, safe slow movements under hold-to-run control may be provided
- Guards also help control metalworking fluid and swarf
- Exhaust ventilation fitted or capable of being connected.

DRILLING (AND REAMING)

HOW MOST ACCIDENTS HAPPEN

▼ Hair caught on rotating spindles, chucks or tools

▼ Entanglement of gloves, clothing, bandages and rings, usually at the drill tip

▼ Violent spinning of the workpiece because of poor clamping - causing scalping injuries, broken bones

▼ Not wearing eye protection causing eye injuries from machine cleaning, swarf removal and unenclosed machining

▼ Swarf - causing cuts

Most **ILL HEALTH** arises from:

▼ unsafe handling (see pages 12-17)

▼ harmful metalworking fluids (see pages 36-37)

▼ too much noise (see pages 38-42)

but in particular risks from handling and metalworking fluids may be higher at manually operated machines used for batch production because of more frequent loading/unloading and contact with fluids.

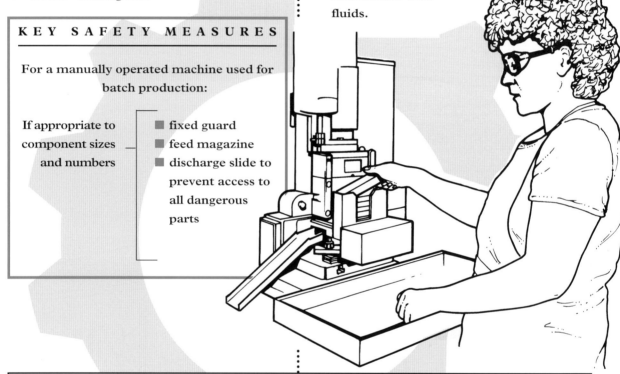

KEY SAFETY MEASURES

For a manually operated machine used for batch production:

If appropriate to component sizes and numbers —

■ fixed guard
■ feed magazine
■ discharge slide to prevent access to all dangerous parts

TRAINING SPECIFICS

In addition to general rules for safe operation (see page 30) users should be trained:

■ to wear eye protection, and

NOT

■ to wear jewellery, loose clothing or long hair not tied back
■ to wear gloves unless complete enclosure of rotating chucks, spindles and attached rotating parts is provided
■ to leave chuck keys in chucks.

KEY REFERENCES: Guidance Note PM83 *Drilling machines: Guarding of spindles and attachments* **HSE Books ISBN 0 7176 1546 4**

BS EN 12717: 2001 *Machine tools - Safety - Drilling machines*

KEY SAFETY MEASURES

For a small CNC drilling machine:

■ Sliding interlocking guards to prevent dangerous movements when guards are open

■ If access to machine movements is necessary when the guards are open, safer, slower movements under hold-to-run control may be permitted

■ Exhaust ventilation fitted or capable of being connected.

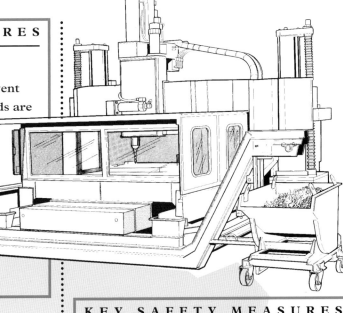

KEY SAFETY MEASURES

For a maually operated radial arm drilling machine:

■ Use suitable tripping device and regularly check its operation

■ Vertical trip not more than 75 mm from the tool and positioned within the first 90° of rotation from the operator's position

■ Clamp workpiece securely to machine table

■ Alternatively fixed, adjustable guards may be used.

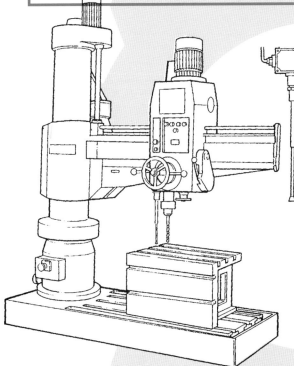

KEY SAFETY MEASURES

For a small maually operated bench drilling machine used for a variety of one-off jobs:

■ Fixed adjustable guard adjusted so that spindle and drill tip is guarded to the greatest extent practicable

■ Vice clamped securely to table.

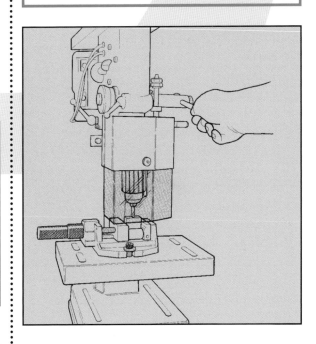

PRESSING

HOW MOST ACCIDENTS HAPPEN

▼ Fingers or hand are amputated or crushed between closing tools
- when loading and unloading components
- when setting up.

Most **ILL HEALTH** arises from:

▼ unsafe handling (see page 12-17) and too much noise (see pages 38-42), but in particular

▼ noise from the impact of tools on workpieces, air ejection, and

▼ handling of workpieces during highly repetitive batch production.

PROVISION AND USE OF WORK EQUIPMENT REGULATIONS 1998 AS APPLIED TO POWER PRESSES

BY LAW every metalworking press and press brake with a flywheel and clutch and its guards must be thoroughly examined by a competent person[†]:

- before use on first installation, whether new or secondhand
- periodically, presses with only fixed guards every 12 months; other presses: every 6 months

Reports of defects must be notified in writing to factory occupiers and copied to the enforcing authority.

SETTERS who prepare presses for use:

■ must be:
   competent
   specifically designated in writing
   properly trained

■ must carry out an inspection of safety devices
- after any work on the tools which involves any alteration to or disturbance of any safety device
- not later than four hours after the start of each working day or shift

■ must sign a certificate, kept near the press, that safety devices are in efficient working order.

[†]from an insurance company, for example

All other presses, including hydraulic and pneumatic, should have similar arrangements to achieve the same objectives - a planned, regular system of inspections and tests by competent and authorised persons to enable the safety of the press and its safety devices to be regularly signed for by an authorised person on behalf of the company.

These inspections may be carried out as described on page 31 under the regulation inspection requirements of PUWER.

KEY SAFETY MEASURES

For a mechanical press:
■ Guards as noise enclosures
■ Loading/unloading components without access between tools using automatic feed.

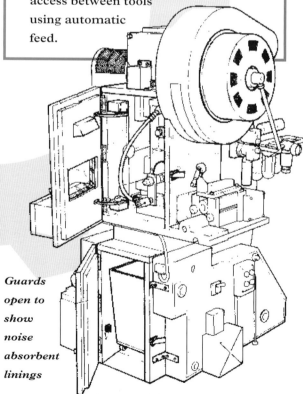

Guards open to show noise absorbent linings

KEY REFERENCE: *Safe use of power presses* **L112 ISBN 0 7176 1627 4**

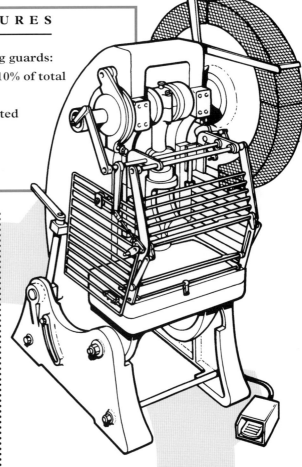

KEY SAFETY MEASURES

For a mechanical power press using interlocking guards:
- Ensure that closing gates overlap by at least 10% of total movement before clutch can be operated
- Prevent loose and slack movement of connected parts of the guard by good maintenance
- Shroud foot pedals
- Repair distorted or damaged bars.

KEY SAFETY MEASURES

For a hydraulic press brake using photoelectric guards:
- Ensure that the back and sides of the press are guarded and that no-one can stand between the light curtain and machine, or reach under, around or over the light curtain or guards to dangerous parts
- Ensure that photoelectric light curtain when interrupted brings downward movement to a halt before dangerous parts can be reached
- Muting (switching the beam off to permit metal sheets to be inserted and bent through the light curtain) must only occur when there is a safe distance* between the bottom of the top tool and the top surface of the component.

KEY SAFETY MEASURES

For a pneumatic hand-fed bench press using interlocking guards:
- Chairs used by operators should be adjusted to the right height and provide good support for the back. Provide foot rests
- Stillages should be positioned to minimise twisting and turning when lifting and lowering components
- Use two pneumatic circuits to control and check interlocking functions or an automatic scotch to prevent tools closing when guards are open
- Ensure overlap of guard and table before press will operate
- Interlock the pneumatic power supply to the press with the movement of the guard.

KEY REFERENCES: BS EN 692: 1996; BS EN 693: 2001; BS EN 12622: 2001

TURNING

HOW MOST ACCIDENTS HAPPEN

▼ A fatal accident arising from entanglement on rotating parts happens every year or so in the UK

▼ Entanglements on workpieces, chucks, carriers and unguarded stock bars cause most accidents

▼ Many accidents happen using hand-held emery cloth to smooth and polish components

▼ Direct contact with moving parts causes many injuries

▼ Eye injuries from machine cleaning, swarf removal and unenclosed machining when eye protection is not worn are frequent

▼ Chuck keys ejected from rotating chucks.

A large proportion of injuries result in amputation of fingers, broken bones and torn ligaments.

Most **ILL HEALTH** arises from:

▼ unsafe handling (see pages 12-17), harmful metalworking fluids (see pages 36-37) and too much noise (see pages 38-42), but in particular

▼ noise levels from stock bars rotating in stock bar tubes which can be very high, particularly on multi-spindle machines

▼ risks from breathing in mists and aerosols may be higher at higher speed machines, and throughout the workshop from groups of machines operating together.

If required surface finish or dimensional accuracy cannot be achieved by turning techniques, consider using dedicated grinding, honing or polishing machines as appropriate instead of hand-held emery cloth.

KEY SAFETY MEASURES

For a small CNC turning machine:

■ Sliding interlocking guards to prevent access to dangerous movements when guards are open

■ If access to machine movements is necessary when guards are open, safer, slower movements under hold to run control may be permitted when guards are open

■ Exhaust extraction fitted or capable of being connected.

■ A strong properly maintained vision panel, capable of withstanding foreseeable ejections.

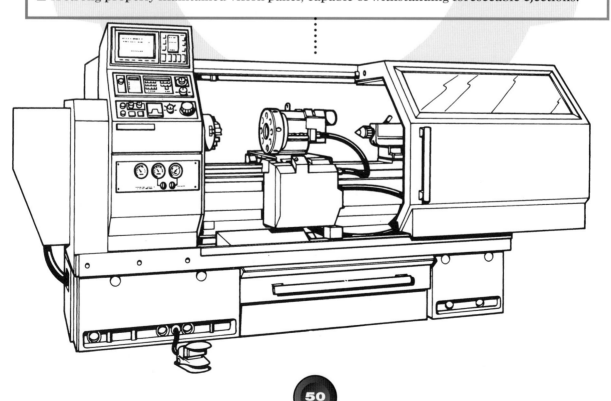

TURNING

TRAINING SPECIFICS

- Wear eye protection
- Don't wear jewellery, loose clothing or long hair if it's not tied back.

If using emery cloth cannot be avoided, in addition to general rules for safe operation (see page 30), users should be trained about the dangers of using emery cloth:

- Never use emery cloth at CNC lathes
- If required finish may only be obtained holding emery cloth against rotating components,
  then use:
  - a backing board
  - a tool post
  - a 'nutcracker'
  - hand-held abrasive-impregnated wire brushes.

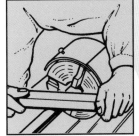

Backing board

Tool post

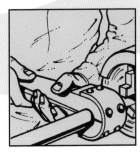

'Nutcracker'

KEY REFERENCES: BS EN 12415: 2000; 12478: 2001; 12840: 2001; 13788: 2001
Accidents at metalworking lathes using emery cloth **EIS2 HSE Books (free)**

GRINDING

HOW MOST ACCIDENTS HAPPEN

▼ Injuries from contact with rotating abrasive wheels

▼ Impact injuries from bursting wheels, (sometimes fatal)

▼ Cutting and crushing injuries from trapping between the wheel and workrest

▼ Fires and explosions arise from the poor control of grinding dust containing aluminium magnesium and similar materials

▼ Eye injuries from the failure to wear eye protection or use protective screens.

Most **ILL HEALTH** arises from:

▼ unsafe handling (see pages 12-17), harmful metalworking fluids (see pages 36-37)

▼ vibration from hand fed or hand-held grinding machines which may cause a condition called vibration white finger, which damages hands and arms, sometimes permanently (see page 43)

▼ too much noise from the grinding operation itself (see pages 38-42) and

▼ inhaling the harmful dust/fume generated.

TIPS FOR OPERATORS

As well as general rules for safe operation (see page 30), users should be trained:

■ to use the right wheel and machine for the job

■ not to grind on the sides of straight-sided wheels used for off hand grinding

■ to keep wheels used for off hand grinding trued and dressed to reduce out of balance and enable workrests to be adjusted close to the wheel

■ to lubricate spindles regularly

■ to run new wheels free for about a minute with persons standing clear

■ to support heavy workpieces and use jigs to reduce vibration at pedestal and bench grinding machines used frequently for long periods (see page 43) particularly for tool sharpening

■ not to stop wheels by applying pressure to the wheel periphery or face

■ not to leave wheels immersed in coolant which may lead to out of balance; coolant should be switched off before wheels are stopped to enable them to dry

■ to take care not to insert oversize components into centreless grinders to minimise risks of ejection and whee breakage

■ to use wheel dressers which minimise risks of vibration white finger.

THE LAW* ON ABRASIVE WHEELS *outlined*

The specific risks associated with mounting abrasive wheels require that such tasks are only done by people who have been specifically designated to do so. Adequate training must be provided for people mounting abrasive wheels. Such training should include:

■ hazards arising from the use of abrasive wheels and precautions which should be observed

■ methods of marking abrasive wheels as to type and speed

■ methods of storing, handling and transporting abrasive wheels

■ methods of inspecting and testing abrasive wheels to check for damage

■ the functions of all components used with abrasive wheels, including flanges, blotters, brushes and nuts used in mounting and including knowledge of the correct and incorrect methods of assembling all components and correct balancing of abrasive wheels

■ the proper method of dressing abrasive wheels

■ the adjustment of the rest of an abrasive wheel.

* Provision and Use of Work Equipment Regulations 1998, Regulation 7

KEY REFERENCES: *Safety in the use of abrasive wheels* HSG17 2000 HSE Books ISBN 0 7176 1739 4; BS EN 13218: 2001 *Machine tools - Safety - Stationary grinding machines*

GRINDING

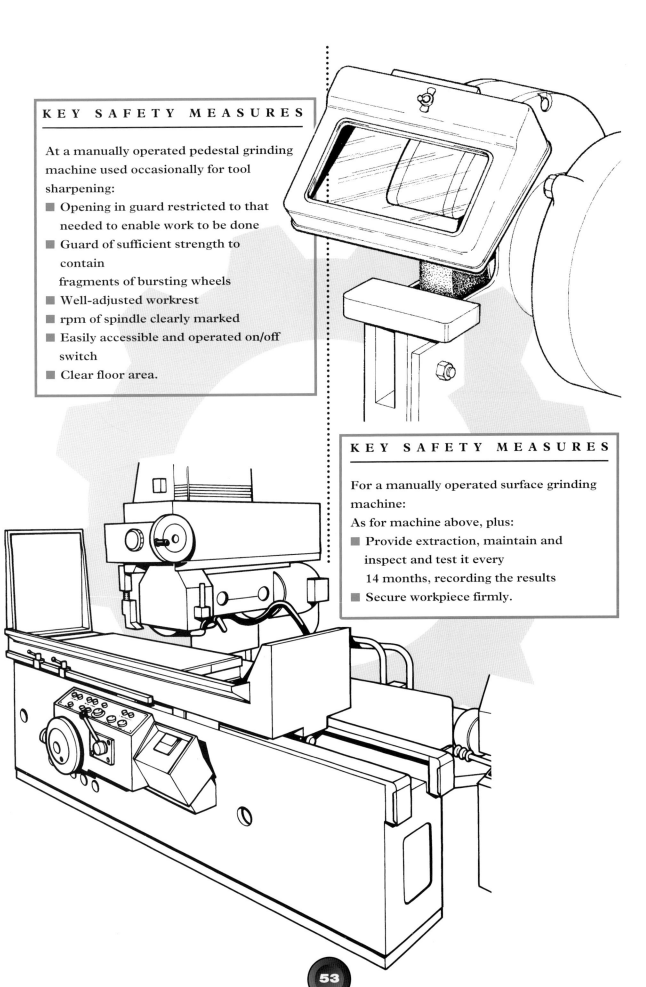

KEY SAFETY MEASURES

At a manually operated pedestal grinding machine used occasionally for tool sharpening:
- Opening in guard restricted to that needed to enable work to be done
- Guard of sufficient strength to contain
  fragments of bursting wheels
- Well-adjusted workrest
- rpm of spindle clearly marked
- Easily accessible and operated on/off switch
- Clear floor area.

KEY SAFETY MEASURES

For a manually operated surface grinding machine:
As for machine above, plus:
- Provide extraction, maintain and inspect and test it every
  14 months, recording the results
- Secure workpiece firmly.

SAWING
USING MANUALLY-FED PIVOTING-HEAD METAL-CUTTING CIRCULAR SAWS

HOW MOST ACCIDENTS HAPPEN

▼ Contact with the running saw blade when:

● feeding, adjusting or removing worpieces

● cleaning the machine or removing swarf.

Most **ILL HEALTH** arises from:

▼ unsafe handling (see pages 12-17)

▼ harmful metalworking fluids (see pages 36-37) and

▼ too much noise (see pages 38-42) from the action of the blade against the workpiece

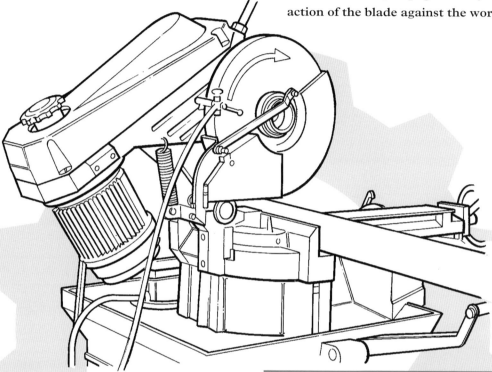

NOISE

Noise high enough to damage hearing is common at many saws, especially high-speed saws for non-ferrous (eg aluminium) cutting.

Reduce at source by, for example:
■ clamping workpieces securely
■ using noise/vibration absorbing materials on feed tables
■ avoiding the use of 'damaged' saw blades
■ enclosing the cutting head in noise absorbing materials
■ using 'damped' saw blades

KEY SAFETY MEASURES

■ Fixed adjustable guards
■ Linkage operated moving guard to prevent
  ● contact with the blade in the raised position
  ● exposure of the blade during cutting
■ Gravity operated guards may only be used with hold to run controls
■ Where fixed guards only are used, workpieces should be fed and removed through openings small enough to prevent access to blades
■ Ensure the head spring balance (if fitted) is properly adjusted.

Training in good sawing technique may help minimise handling problems and noise.

KEY REFERENCES: *Safety at manually-fed pivoting-head metal-cutting circular saws* **EIS12 HSE Books (free)** **BS EN 13898: 2003** *Machine tools - Safety - Sawing machines for cold metal*

BENDING USING 3 ROLL BENDING MACHINES

HOW MOST ACCIDENTS HAPPEN

▼ Hands are frequently drawn into counter-rotating rollers, particularly during initial feeding of the workpiece

▼ Hands are often trapped between a workpiece and a roller

▼ Wearing gloves increases the risks of trapping

▼ Many injuries are serious; amputations are not uncommon

KEY SAFETY MEASURES

■ Hold to run controls should automatically return to stop on release

■ Braking may be required to achieve a safe stopping time

■ Position trip devices to be easily activated by any person drawn towards them at both sides of the machine to bring it to a stop before serious injury

■ Emergency stop buttons requiring manual reset after use

■ Use feed tables and rollers to help avoid gripping workpieces close to the rolls.

Most **ILL HEALTH** arises from:

▼ unsafe feeding/unloading of workpieces which are too heavy/sharp/awkward (see pages 12-17)

TRAINING SPECIFICS

In addition to general rules for safe operation (see page 30), users should be trained to:

■ not wear gloves during the initial feeding of workpieces

■ avoid gripping workpieces close to the rolls; feed tables and rollers can help

■ avoid slips and trips around the machine by keeping the area clear

■ clear rolls and maintain only when the machine is switched off and isolated.

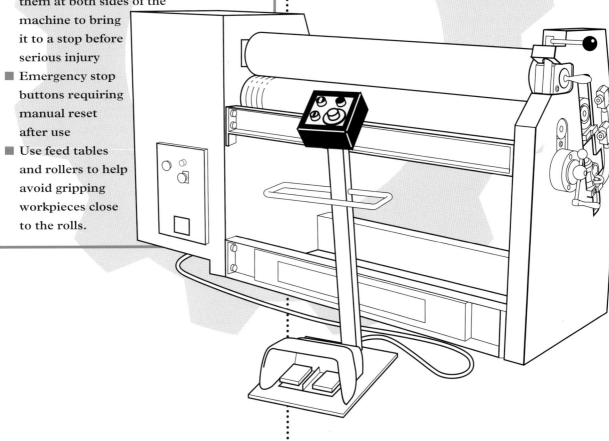

KEY REFERENCE: *Safeguarding 3 roll bending machines* EIS7(rev1) HSE Books (free)

GUILLOTINING

HOW MOST ACCIDENTS HAPPEN

▼ Feeding and removing workpieces near unguarded blades at the front, sides and rear of machines causing cut and amputated fingers.

KEY SAFETY MEASURES

For a medium-sized power guillotine:
■ Opening in front guard insufficient to reach clamp(s) or blade
■ Built in lighting and marker to see cutting line
■ Sloped discharge chute to enable workpieces to be retrieved without opening guard.
■ Rear interlocking guard
■ Shrouded foot pedal.

Noise may be reduced by:
■ noise hoods
■ rollers to reduce vibrations during sheet feeding
■ rubber bases fitted to clamps
■ minimising the distance workpieces and scrap fall
■ lining bins with noise absorbent material.

Reduce **cuts** from handling by providing good quality gloves, such as chromed leather.

Most **ILL HEALTH** arises from

▼ unsafe handling (see pages 12-17), particularly heavy and/or sharp edged workpieces
▼ too much noise (see pages 38-42), particularly from cut workpieces falling, clamping and cutting operations, and high speed continuous shearing.

TRAINING SPECIFICS

In addition to general rules for safe operation and maintenance (see page 30), operators and others should know how to:
■ work safely at the rear of guillotines fitted with powered back gauges and mechanical handling devices, particularly on CNC machines, where control systems may be complex
■ change blades safely
■ maintain powered machines to prevent blades dropping under gravity.

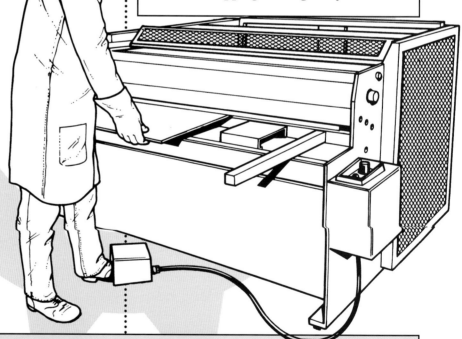

Special attention should be paid to the safety of young people (under the age of 18) using guillotines. The law* requires that employers assess risks to young people before they start work, taking into account their inexperience, lack of awareness of potential risks and their immaturity. You should take account of the risk assessment in determining whether the young person should use the equipment. Proper training and supervision will be essential.

*Management of Health and Safety at Work Regulations 1992, regulation 3.

KEY REFERENCE: *Safety in the use of metal cutting guillotines and shears*
HSG42 HSE Books ISBN 0 11 885455 0

CNC PUNCH PRESSING

HOW MOST ACCIDENTS HAPPEN

▼ Between the tools during tool changing, cleaning and fault finding, causing crushing injuries to the hands

▼ at moving tables, causing lacerations to fingers.

Most **ILL HEALTH** arises from

▼ unsafe handling (see pages 12-17) and too much noise (see pages 38-42), but particularly from:

▼ handling large and/or sharp edged workpieces

▼ noise from tool impacts.

KEY SAFETY MEASURES

For a CNC punch press:

■ Turret guarding by fixed and interlocking guards to permit, when open, only slower movements under hold-to-run control

■ Leave a safe distance between moving parts/workpieces and fixed structures

■ Hazardous areas may be safeguarded by fixed perimeter fences with interlocking access gates and/or pressure sensitive mats and/or presence sensing devices to prevent dangerous parts moving where persons have access to them

■ Where turret guard and table do not prevent access to closing punch tools safety devices such as pressure sensitive mats or photo-electric guards should be provided

■ Large tool carousels and changers should be safeguarded by fixed and interlocking guards or equivalent means which may also prevent access to traps between moving sheets and tool gaps in the table

■ Safety devices may be overridden to permit machine movements at slow speeds under hold- to-run control, for setting or maintenance.

NOISE

may be reduced by:

■ using cushioned or anti-vibration mountings

■ ensuring the right shear angle on tools

■ using non-metallic clamping faces

■ enclosure of the tool area.

COMBINATION METALWORKING MACHINES

HOW MOST ACCIDENTS HAPPEN

▼ Working small workpieces at a workstation, resulting in amputations of fingers.

KEY SAFETY MEASURES

■ Guards should:
- prevent access to closing tools, punches or blades from all sides
- provide a view of the operation where needed

■ Workpieces should be properly supported by guides and stops

■ The take off side should also be guarded to allow only workpieces to pass through

■ Do not take off pieces by hand:
- use a chute which discharges into a box for smaller pieces
- and a table or roller track for larger ones.

When bending, either restrict the gap between the tools to a safe distance (see pages 49 and 108) or provide photo-electric or other safeguards as for press brakes (see page 49).

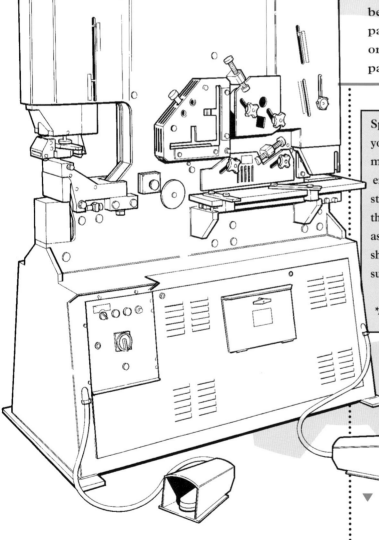

Special attention should be paid to the safety of young people (under the age of 18) using combination metalworking machines. The law* requires that employers assess risks to young people before they start work, taking into account their inexperience and their immaturity. You should take account of the risk assessment in determining whether the young person should use the equipment. Proper training and supervision will be essential.

*Management of Health and Safety at Work Regulations 1992, Regulation 3.

Most **ILL HEALTH** arises from
▼ unsafe handling (see pages 12-17) and too much noise (see pages 38-42), but particularly from:
▼ handling large and/or sharp edged workpieces
▼ noise from tool impacts.

KEY REFERENCE: *Safeguarding of combination metalworking machines* **EIS13(rev)**
HSE Books (free)

HORIZONTAL BORING MACHINES

HOW MOST ACCIDENTS HAPPEN

▼ Most injuries occur during activities such as setting/adjustment, swarf removal, or observation for the purpose of process control.

▼ The largest single cause of injury is entanglement at revolving tools.

▼ Crushing and trapping hazards at tools and the moving worktable are also very significant causes of injury.

▼ Injuries are often very severe and include limb and skull fractures and amputations. The potential for fatal injury at these machines should not be underestimated.

Most **ILL HEALTH** arises from

▼ unsafe handling (see pages 12-17)

▼ harmful metalworking fluids (see pages 36-37)

KEY SAFETY MEASURES

■ Prevent access to the work zone by fixed and/or interlocked guards.

■ Trip probes with breaking devices may be used in some circumstances, but these will only provide limited protection, stopping the machine quickly in the event of contact with revolving tools. They do not provide protection against crushing and trapping hazards.

■ Where access to the work zone is needed for setting purposes, dangerous machine movements should be controlled using a hold-to-run control arrangement or enabling device.

■ Guard other hazardous parts such as transmission elements including shafts, gears, pulleys etc using fixed guards.

■ Follow safe systems of work for cleaning, maintenance, setting and adjustment, loading of workpieces etc. Activities such as swarf removal should normally be carried out with the spindle stopped.

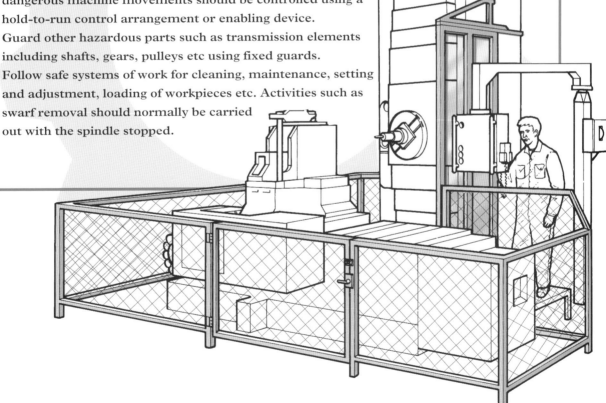

KEY REFERENCE: *Safeguarding at horizontal boring machines* EIS28
HSE Books (free); BS EN 13128: 2001

CLEANING AND DEGREASING

Many cleaning and degreasing substances used are hamful if not used properly, either through direct skin or eye contact or through breathing in mist or vapour given off, commonly causing dermatitis and narcotic effects. Some cleaners give off vapour which is easily ignited.

TO MINIMISE HAZARDS:

▼ reduce the need to clean by, for example, avoiding contamination in the first place

▼ compare safety data sheets from suppliers to find the least harmful cleaner and the cleaner which is non-flammable or the least flammable (with a higher flashpoint) (different hazards posed by solvents may need to be balanced to ensure that overall, hazards to health and safety are minimised)

▼ avoid spills and evaporation by keeping lids on containers and transferring liquids between containers by pipework or pump

▼ mark stores and their contents clearly

▼ provide appropriate personal protective equipment such as gloves, overalls, eye and foot protection, to prevent contact where necessary

▼ you may need to draw up an emergency plan (see page 78) to cope with gross spillages of some cleaning and degreasing substances.

WHEN USING LIQUIDS TO CLEAN by dipping, wiping or spraying:

▼ avoid halogenated solvents such as trichloroethylene ('trike'). perchloro ethylene ('perk') methylene chloride and n-propyl bromide (nPB) unless they are enclosed and extraction ventilation and other necessary protective equipment is provided; other solvents may also need similar controls

▼ use the least flammable (with flashpoints ideally above 45^0C) hydrocarbon solvents such as petroleum distillates, terpenes and alcohols

▼ adopt precautions necessary to minimise risks from contact with alkaline or acid water-based solutions or inhalation of fume or dust arising from them

▼ avoid work in confined spaces (inside metal fabrications for example) unless absolutely necessary in which case make a separate special assessment of the hazards posed by the cleaning liquid and system of work proposed. (Special precautions, including compressed airline breathing apparatus, a safety harness and a second person standing by, may be necessary, see page 62.)

KEY REFERENCE: *Safe use of solvent degreasing plant* EIS40
HSE Books (free); *Maintenance and cleaning of solvent degreasing plant EIS20(rev1)*

VAPOUR DEGREASING TANKS

USING THEM badly may expose operators and others to harmful levels of vapour which if inhaled can cause drowsiness and in extreme cases unconsciousness or even death. Direct contact with the vapour or liquid can cause irritation and dermatitis, and should never be frequent or prolonged.

Solvent degreasing should be carried out in an enclosed system where reasonably practicable. Otherwise, the process should be enclosed as far as possible.

To minimise exposure:
DO:
- position tank in an area free from draughts
- stack components inside the degreaser so they drain properly
- allow them to dry in the freeboard zone before removing them
- use covers when not using the tank
- use a mechanical hoist when loading/unloading components.

DON'T:
- move, load or remove components too quickly, pushing or dragging vapour out
- run hoists at more than three metres per minute vertically
- spray above the vapour layer.

MAINTENANCE minimises risks to operators and others:

▼ from escaping vapour

▼ from the build up of oil and grease which can catch fire

▼ and can **prevent the need to enter** in order to remove baked-on residues. Getting into vapour degreasing tanks causes a sizeable proportion of all fatal accidents in small engineering workshops.

Always:
- set thermostats correctly and balance heating and cooling systems
- check and maintain the effectiveness of extraction systems
- pump in fluid below the existing liquid level
- repair leaks
- treat pits in which degreasing tanks are set as extensions of the tank itself
- maintain the correct solvent level
- check the solvent condition
- ensure adequate freeboard height
- ensure the bath has a bottom drain for removing solvent.

KEY REFERENCE: *Surface cleaning and preparation: Choosing the best option* **GG354**
Available free from Envirowise on Environment and Energy Helpline Tel: 0800 585794;
Website: www.envirowise.gov.uk

VAPOUR DEGREASING TANKS

TO AVOID ENTRY:

▼ Fix a sign on or near the degreaser prohibiting entry without authorisation and breathing equipment

▼ Regularly monitor contamination by measuring the temperature of boiling solvent; distil off solvent into a storage drum; drain mobile residues into a suitable container, and

▼ Use a long-handled scraper to remove remaining sludge, or

▼ Pump dirty solvent directly into a container for recovery.

THE LAW* ON ENTRY INTO DEGREASERS

No person shall enter a degreasing tank for any purpose (such as to clean it), unless it is not reasonably practicable to achieve that purpose without such entry. If a degreasing tank is entered, this must be done in accordance with a safe system of work that allows it to be done safely and without risks to health.

*Confined Spaces Regulations 1997

IF ENTRY CANNOT BE AVOIDED

▼ Establish a safe system of work in writing using a formal permit-to-work system for entry authorised by a responsible person

▼ Remove as much solvent and sludge as possible before entering

▼ Use suitable self-contained breathing apparatus or air line compressed air equipment, and
● a safety harness or belt and rope held or secured outside the degreaser to pull the person out if necessary
● a second person standing by to raise the alarm and start the rescue (it is unlikely that one person could pull someone out single-handedly - have a rescue plan ready)

▼ Provide additional breathing apparatus and other suitable protective equipment capable of being used for rescue

▼ Make oxygen resuscitation equipment immediately available

▼ Wear protective clothing resistant to the solvent involved

▼ Check and maintain breathing apparatus and air line compressed air equipment, harnesses and lifelines at least once a month, and keep records

▼ Fully train all who may become involved.

If, while all the above precautions are being taken:
▼ the tank is thoroughly cleaned, tested and certified as safe for entry, and

▼ an adequate supply of breathable air is maintained

breathing apparatus may not be needed for further work (but see page 60, final paragraph, and pages 63-65, *Welding*).

KEY REFERENCE: *Maintenance and cleaning of solvent degreasing plant* EIS20(rev1) HSE Books (free)

WELDING AND FLAMECUTTING

Common causes of **ILL HEALTH** are:

▼ inhalation of harmful welding fume

▼ unsafe handling of workpieces and welding equipment, particularly gas cylinders

▼ noise, particularly from plasma arc cutting, gouging operations and weld preparation

▼ burn from ultra violet radiation, including 'arc eye'

▼ vibration during grinding for weld preparation

▼ discomfort from heat and uncomfortable postures.

COMMON CAUSES OF ACCIDENTS ARE:

As a result of:

▼ falling gas cylinders

▼ particles entering unprotected eyes during chipping after welding

▼ electric shocks from arc welding equipment

▼ fires started by flames, sparks and hot material from welding and cutting processes

▼ fingers being crushed between the electrodes of fixed resistance welding machines

KEY SAFETY MEASURES

for arc welding:

■ Extraction equipment

■ Provide appropriate protective clothing and ensure it is worn, eg overalls, protective apron, gloves, safety boots, respiratory protection (if necessary)

■ Use welding screens and eye protection (to BS 679) to prevent arc eye

■ Local isolation switch

■ Welding set transformer

■ Workpiece earth when required

■ Insulated electrode holder

■ Insulated box for electrode holder

■ Proper cable connections

■ Suitable fire extinguisher easily accessible

■ Welding leads should be insulated, robustly constructed and big enough to carry the current safely

■ Residual current devices may enhance safety

■ Work in confined spaces and on large structures supported on manipulating devices needs special precautions (see *Further reading*, page 87).

TRAINING SPECIFICS

for arc welders:

■ Know how to use extraction equipment

■ Do not wear metallic jewellery, rings, or watch straps

■ Know how to change electrodes safely

■ Use an insulated box or hook to rest the electrode holder NOT the face shield, clothing or rags.

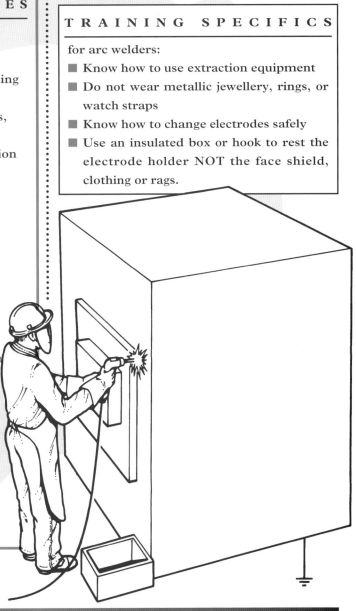

KEY REFERENCE:

Electrical safety in arc welding HSG118 HSE Books ISBN 0 7176 0704 6

WELDING AND FLAMECUTTING

Maintain welding ventilation and protective equipment

▼ Have local exhaust ventilation examined and tested by a competent person every 14 months (see page 21)

▼ Examine respiratory protective equipment thoroughly every month (testing air fed equipment at the same intervals, checking the volume and quality of breathing air supplied)

▼ Examine flexible gas and oxygen hoses regularly and replace damaged ones; never repair them with tape

▼ Check and maintain other safeguards as appropriate.

NEVER APPLY heat to containers, tanks or drums which may contain flammable residues. Either use cold, non-sparking methods or clean and make them gas free first.

Store and use welding gas cylinders safely

▼ Store full and empty cylinders in a safe, well-ventilated place preferably outside buildings

▼ Never keep cylinders below ground level next to drains, basements and other low-lying places - heavy gases will not disperse easily

▼ Do not leave charged hoses where ventilation is poor for extended periods in case of leaking gases or oxygen

▼ Some gas cylinders, for example acetylene, contain liquid - store them with their valves uppermost

▼ Protect cylinders from damage, for example by chaining unstable cylinders in racks or on trolleys

▼ Provide suitable trolleys with restraining chains for moving oxy-acetylene sets and other cylinders

▼ Minimise damage by using the correct hoses, clamps, couples and regulators for the particular gas and appliance being used

▼ Never apply grease oil or other lubricants to oxygen fittings

▼ Prevent damage to hoses. Do not run them unprotected, for example, across traffic routes

▼ Turn off cylinder valves at the end of each day's work

▼ Change cylinders away from sources of ignition in a well-ventilated place

▼ Minimise welding flame 'flash-back' into hoses or cylinders by training operators in correct lighting up and working procedures and by fitting effective non-return valves and flame arresters

▼ Use soap or detergent and water solutions to test for leaks - **NEVER A FLAME**

▼ Do not use oxygen as a substitute for compressed air to power pneumatic tools.

KEY REFERENCE: *The safe use of compressed gases in welding, flame cutting and allied processes* HSG139 HSE Books ISBN 0 7176 0680 5

CONTROL OF FUME AND GASES AT WELDING, FLAMECUTTING

AND SIMILAR PROCESSES SUCH AS BRAZING AND SOLDERING

Fume from welding, flamecutting, brazing and soldering varies greatly in composition and concentration. Different jobs lead to different levels of exposure to different susbtances. Fume from welding and flame cutting may cause:

▼ dryness of the throat, tickling, coughing, tightness of the chest and difficulty in breathing

▼ an acute flu-like illness (metal fume fever)

▼ long-term changes in the lung.

Welding or cutting processes releasing the greatest quantities of harmful fume include:

▼ work on metallic coatings such as cadmium or zinc plating and chromium, manganese, cobalt and/or nickel hard surfaces

▼ work on painted surfaces which contain lead, zinc, chromium or cadmium pigments

▼ mechanised flame cutting

▼ flame gouging

▼ frequent and regular manual metal arc welding

▼ flux cored electrode welding

▼ higher current metal inert gas shielded welding particularly on stainless steel, and aluminium, copper, nickel and their alloys

▼ oxygen arc cutting and gouging

▼ using cadmium-containing solder.

MINIMISE RISKS by:

▼ avoiding welding and flamecutting, using other bonding and cutting techniques where reasonably practicable

▼ using safer filler materials, such as cadmium free silver solder

▼ controlling exhaust fume by providing local exhaust ventilation unless a detailed and thorough risk assessment shows that harmful fume is not being generated or that it may be controlled by general ventilation

▼ providing respiratory protective equipment, but only if control measures are unable to reduce fumes to safe levels

▼ ensuring workshops have enough low-level inlets and high-level outlets for air changes

▼ not welding near (10 m for most welding; 20 m for aluminium) cleaning processes using chlorinated solvents; the heat and arc from welding may break down the solvents into more harmful substances.

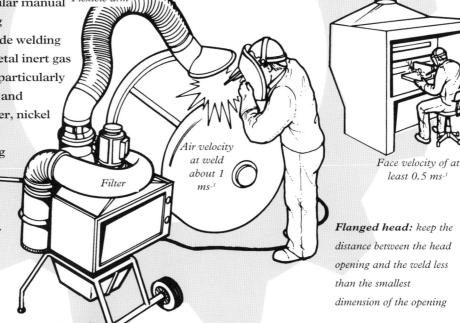

Flexible arm

Filter

Air velocity at weld about 1 ms⁻¹

Face velocity of at least 0.5 ms⁻¹

Flanged head: *keep the distance between the head opening and the weld less than the smallest dimension of the opening*

MOBILE EXTRACTION

Consider on-gun extraction particularly with semi– automatic Mig welding guns and flux cored wires without gas shielding.

WELDING BENCH/BOOTH

Extracted air may be filtered electro-statically, for example, and returned to the workshop to prevent heat losses.

SAFETY MEASURES AT RESISTANCE WELDING MACHINES

HOW MOST ACCIDENTS HAPPEN

▼ Trapping between the electrodes, causing crushed and amputated finger tips

▼ Spatter flying into unprotected eyes.

Most **ILL HEALTH** arises from the unsafe handling of workpieces (see pages 12–17), and too much noise (see pages 38-42), particularly from groups of machines together.

K E Y   S A F E T Y   M E A S U R E S

for fixed resistance welding machines:

■ Fit an effective screen to protect eyes. Use eye protection if this is not possible

■ Limit the gap between the electrodes to 6 mm or less where practicable

■ Where the operator does not need to hold the component, use:
  ● interlocking guards or non-contact, eg photoelectric, protective devices with fixed guards
  ● or, where these are not practicable, two-hand control

■ Where the operator needs to hold the component
  ● use sensing or low pressure approach systems to prevent full closing pressure of the welding heads until within a safe distance of the component. If the operator uses one hand to support the component, use a remote operating button and not a footswitch.

■ Always shroud foot pedals.

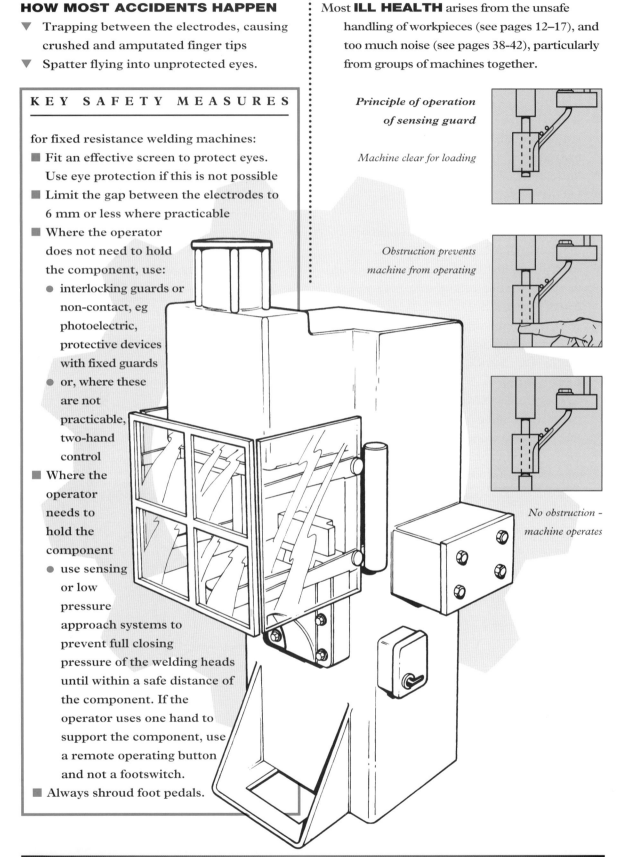

Principle of operation of sensing guard

Machine clear for loading

Obstruction prevents machine from operating

No obstruction – machine operates

KEY REFERENCE: *Safeguarding of resistance welding machines*
Information Document HSE ID 668/23 (see www.hse.gov.uk/fod/infodocs/668_23.pdf)

LASERS USED FOR WELDING AND CUTTING

The most serious **HAZARDS** arise from exposure to:

▼ laser radiation either direct or reflected from process materials or surroundings which may cause severe tissue damage. The eye is particularly vulnerable with the greatest risk arising from Nd-YAG lasers.

▼ fume, which may harm breathing (see page 65)

▼ contact with live electrical parts during maintenance, which may cause burns and/or shock (CO_2 lasers operate at extremely high voltages which may remain lethal because of stored energy after isolation of the electrical supply)

▼ dangerous machine movements which may physically injure.

Laser emissions may also be a fire hazard, especially where powers exceed a few watts.

IEC 60825-1: 1993 (Edition 1: 1993 consolidated with amendments 1: 1997 and 2: 2001) - *Safety of laser products*, available from BSI, is a comprehensive introduction for manufacturers and users to the reduction of risks from laser radiation. The maximum permissible exposure limits (MPE) given in this standard are regarded as reasonably practicable limits to be achieved under the Health and Safety at Work etc Act 1974, Sections 2, 3 and 6.

KEY SAFETY MEASURES

Make sure the right SAFETY MEASURES and information for use have been supplied. (Question your supplier in the first instance if there is anything you are not sure of.)

Maintain in particular:
■ anti-scatter guards at cutting/welding heads
■ installation enclosures, fixed guards and interlocking access doors to contain reflections from high power machines
■ ventilating equipment
■ safeguards preventing access to dangerous machine movements
■ laser safety eyewear.

TRAINING SPECIFICS

In addition to general rules for safe machine operation and maintenance (see page 30), train users and others to observe the rules for safe:

■ entry into enclosures (use trapped or key exchange systems where provided)
■ beam alignment or adjustment
■ working with electricity
■ use of eye protection where necessary.

KEY REFERENCE: IEC 60825-1: 1993 (including 1997 and 2001 amendments)

RADIOGRAPHY

X-rays, gamma rays and other forms of radiation used for non-destructive testing (NDT) may injure by causing burns, dermatitis, cancer, cell damage, blood changes or cataracts.

THE IONISING RADIATION REGULATIONS 1999 *outlined*

If radiography is carried out in your workshop you (or, if a contractor is doing the work, they) must:

- notify HSE before starting work
- consult a suitable radiation protection adviser
- carry out a prior risk assessment
- arrange for medical examinations/reviews and routine dose assessments of employees whom you designate as "classified persons"
- appoint one or more of your employees to supervise radiation work
- provide local rules and training
- make arrangements to deal with stuck radioactive sources, x-ray exposures failing to terminate, etc and rehearse them.
  Get authorisation for the use, storage and safe disposal of radioactive substances from the Environment Agency/SEPA, as appropriate.

OTHER NON-DESTRUCTIVE TESTING TECHNIQUES, such as magnetic particle and dye penetrant techniques may involve the spraying of harmful solvents. Exposure to harmful levels of such solvents needs to be assessed in line with COSHH (see page 20) and prevented or controlled.

TO MINIMISE RISKS:

▼ always carry out routine radiography of readily moveable articles inside a permanent shielded enclosure, sufficient to limit dose rates outside the enclosure to less than 7.5 microsieverts an hour

▼ make sure there are no people near open-topped enclosures (in offices, or overhead crane cabs, for example) who may be affected

▼ if you change your generator or source you may have to upgrade the enclosure

▼ have to hand an emergency plan and the equipment necessary to put the plan into effect (for radioactive sources to include bags of lead shot, a shielded pot and long-handled tools) and rehearse the plan

▼ wear your dosemeter when required and make sure it is not damaged or exposed to radiation when not being worn

▼ use a maintained and tested radiation dose rate meter to check radiation levels around the controlled area and always use the monitor when approaching the source container to check the that the sealed source has fully retracted or x-ray generator is no longer producing x-rays

▼ maintain radiography controls, for example windouts and guide tubes for sealed source equipment, and warning devices.

IF YOU CAN'T DO THE WORK IN A SHIELDED ENCLOSURE, YOU MUST:

▼ notify HSE at least seven days in advance of each occasion on which you propose to work

▼ plan the work to ensure radiation exposures are suitably restricted by use of collimation and localised shielding, barriers, warning signals, lighting and other means to demarcate the controlled area.

KEY REFERENCE: *Industrial radiography: Managing radiation risks* **IRIS1 (rev1)** available from HSE Books (free)

PAINTING

THE **HAZARDS** OF USING PAINTS,
THINNERS OR SOLVENTS INCLUDE:

- breathing in vapour
- direct skin or eye contact
- swallowing causing irritation and diseases of the skin, eyes and lungs, and
- fires from the ignition of flammable vapours.

The **risks** of harm actually occurring are highest when:

- using paints containing large proportions of toxic materials such as lead or isocyanates
- painting in confined spaces
- spraying in unventilated open workshops.

TO REDUCE RISKS

▼ Use the least hazardous materials for the job (water based paints for example and alternatives to lead for rust prevention are widely available)

▼ Follow the rules for work in confined spaces (see pages 60 and 62) and

▼ Always control spray by using ventilated booths, enclosures or separate workspaces.

Take care with paints by:

▼ using protective clothing and eye protection

▼ using any pre-work barrier or protective conditioning cream provided

▼ removing rings or watches which can trap paint against the skin

▼ taking care with solvents when cleaning brushes, spray guns etc

▼ never eating, drinking or smoking while painting

▼ keeping overalls and respirator in a clean state by regular washing

▼ washing hands before eating, and showering or bathing at the end of the day

▼ leaving protective clothing at work to reduce the risk of harmful substances being taken home.

THE LAW ON THE MAIN HAZARDS ASSOCIATED WITH PAINTING *outlined*

Hazardous substances in paints must be controlled in line with the Control of Substances Hazardous to Health Regulations (see page 20).

The Highly Flammable Liquids and Liquefied Petroleum Gases Regulations 1972 specify steps which must be taken to minimise the risks of igniting vapours from paints and solvents which are classified as highly flammable liquids (flash point less than 32^0C).

Don't forget to obtain a licence for the storage of petroleum products from your local petroleum officer who works for your Fire Brigade or local Tradings Standards Department.

Storing and mixing paints

In order to minimise the flammable (and to some extent other) risks from vapours given off by many paints and solvents:

▼ keep only small quantities (not more than 50 litres) on their own in a metal cupboard or bin for immediate use at the workplace and larger stocks in a fire-resisting store with spillage retention and good ventilation

▼ keep lids on cans and containers closed to stop vapour escaping. Contain spillages by decanting paint over a tray. Have absorbent material readily available to soak up spillages. Keep contaminated material in a lidded metal bin and dispose of its contents safely

▼ exclude sources of ignition and use suitable electrical equipment. Do not smoke where paints are stored or used

▼ ensure adequate ventilation where paints are mixed. Breathing protection may be needed

▼ treat containers emptied of liquid the same as full ones; they will often be full of vapour.

KEY REFERENCES: EIS 32 *Chromate primer paints* HSE Books (free)

SPRAY PAINTING
BOOTHS AND ENCLOSURES

If you make your own spray booth or enclosure:

▼ use fire-resistant materials (see list in Appendix 5)

▼ keep unprotected electrical equipment outside (for example by installing lights outside booths and shining them through fixed and sealed fire resisting wired glass panels)

▼ get advice from a competent ventilation engineer and:

● extract to a safe place in the open air away from people, sources of ignition and nearby buildings and equipment

● use a centrifugal or bifurcated fan (with the motor outside the ducting in a vapour free area driving the fan through a gas tight shaft seal). Use flexible armoured cable for electrical wiring to withstand fan vibration rather than mineral insulated metal sheathed cable

● use filters to prevent deposits of paint on motor casings, fan blades and inside ducts; deposits may cause fans to vibrate and run out of balance and direct deposits may also cause motors to overheat and ignite

● provide access points for inspection and cleaning inside ducting.

To maximise the efficiency of any booth or enclosure:

▼ provide means to indicate when dry filters need replacement. The air speed in the immediate vicinity of the sprayer in a dry filter spray booth or enclosure may be the lowest in the booth because of the accumulation of spray deposits on the filter. Hence the air speed tends to be slowest where it is most needed

▼ keep unnecessary equipment out of booths. Large drums of paint for example can disturb the air flow pattern and cause recirculation of contaminated air into the sprayer's breathing zone

▼ provide sufficient and suitably protected lighting in the booth to remove the temptation to spray outside it

▼ give training in the techniques of spray painting to teach how to spray with the minimum amount of overspray and bounceback, to obtain the correct balance between air and liquid flow rates, and to ensure that the minimum pressure for good atomisation is always used

▼ consider the efficiency of the spraying equipment used. Some equipment generates lower levels of solvent vapour and overspray than others.

KEY REFERENCE: *Introduction to local exhaust ventilation HSG37*
HSE Books ISBN 0 7176 1001 2

SPRAY PAINTING
Booths and enclosures

MAINTAINING BOOTHS AND ENCLOSURES:

▼ Check booths and enclosures regularly for leaks, have them thoroughly examined and tested every 14 months by a competent person (eg an insurance company engineering surveyor or representative of the supplier) and keep the reports

▼ Maintain a minimum average air velocity of 0.7 m/s at the front of open-fronted booths and enclosures

▼ Where a sprayer works inside a side draught booth or enclosure the average air velocity where the sprayer stands should be not less than 0.5 m/s with a minimum measured value of 0.4 m/s

▼ The sprayer should never stand between the article being sprayed and the point of extraction; a turntable to rotate articles as necessary should be used

▼ Where a sprayer works inside a down draught booth or enclosure, air velocity (measured to points around a typical article sprayed) should average 0.4 m/s with a minimum measured value of 0.3 m/s

▼ Ensure that airflow or air pressure differential switches are working to warn if designed exhaust ventilation flow rates are not maintained

▼ Maintain any interlocks fitted between spray guns and exhausts ventilation

▼ Repair damaged spray booth and enclosure panels to maintain the fire resistance of the unit

▼ Keep escape routes and access to rescue equipment clear

▼ Ensure that air intakes are not obstructed and that discharge vents are correctly sited and in good repair.

SPRAYING LARGE ARTICLES

Where articles too large to enclose are sprayed use a separate room after:

▼ ensuring adequate half-hour fire resistant separation from adjoining rooms

▼ removing all sources of ignition such as directly fired heaters or domestic-type electric and gas fires and turning off and isolating electrical equipment which is not explosion protected

▼ providing ventilation to a safe place while spraying, and

▼ ensuring adequate personal protection is worn and that no-one else unprotected in the workroom or nearby will be exposed to the spray or vapour.

KEY REFERENCE: *The maintenance, examination and testing of local exhaust* HSG54 HSE Books ISBN 0 7176 1485 9

PAINTS CONTAINING ISOCYANATES

HEALTH HAZARDS

Two-pack spray paints containing isocyanates are often used to achieve hard, durable, easy to clean finishes. In these paints, isocyanate hardeners or activators are added to liquid resin and pigments to produce a polyurethane film.

Vapours and spray mists containing isocyanates are highly irritant to the eyes and respiratory tract and are known to cause asthma. Isocyanates are respiratory sensitisers. This means they can cause an allergic reaction called sensitisation. Once a person is sensitised to isocyanates, further exposure, even to the tiniest trace will cause symptoms, eg:

- sore eyes
- running nose
- sore throat
- coughing
- wheezing, tight chest
- fever and breathlessness.

At first these complaints may clear up at weekends or during holidays, but are likely to return when back at work.

Exposure to isocyanate containing glues during assembly may cause similar problems and require similar avoidance, control and/or protective measures.

HOW CAN HEALTH BE PROTECTED?

▼ Consider non-isocyanate two-pack paints which are available

▼ Assess the hazards and risks and prevent or control exposure in line with the COSHH Regulations (see page 20)

▼ Identify isocyanate-containing two-pack paints from their labels or suppliers' data sheets

▼ If you suffer from chronic respiratory disease such as chronic asthma do not work with two-pack paints containing isocyanates

▼ Consult an occupational health professional before working with isocyanate-containing two-pack paints for advice on a suitable health surveillance programme

▼ Spray only in mechanically ventilated booths or separate workrooms adequately ventilated

▼ Use only mechanically ventilated ovens for accelerating curing. Run them under negative pressure

▼ Ventilate vapour and spray, after filtration, to a safe place in the open air where they will not be drawn back into the workroom or into nearby premises

▼ When mixing and spraying wear protective clothing including gloves and eye protection; wear air fed or compressed airline breathing apparatus (depending on the outcome of your risk assessment) even for small spraying jobs

▼ If a full facepiece canister respirator is worn for mixing or similar jobs change the canister before its recommended life (often as little as 15 minutes) is exceeded. Gauze facemasks do not provide protection

▼ Maintain and keep respiratory protective equipment clean.

KEY REFERENCES: *Safety in motor vehicle repair: Working with 2-pack isocyanate paints* INDG388 HSE Books (single copies free ISBN 0 7176 2756 X for priced packs of 10) *Preventing asthma at work: How to control respiratory sensitisers* L55 HSE Books 1994 ISBN 0 7176 0661 9

POWDER COATING

HEALTH HAZARDS

Powder coating is an alternative finishing process to spray painting. The hazards of using coating powders include:
- direct skin contact with the powders
- breathing in powders in the air
- swallowing powders.

Some curing or hardening agents used in powders, especially TGIC (triglycidl isocyanurate) and TMA (tri-mellitic anhydride) can cause direct irritation of the skin, eyes and lungs or allergic skin reactions. There is concern that some curing agents may cause asthma.

The risks of harm occurring are highest when:
- ▼ using powders containing curing agents such as TGIC or TMA
- ▼ spraying powder in poorly ventilated powder-coating booths
- ▼ following poor systems of work, such as leaning into the coating booth when spraying
- ▼ carrying out powder transfer, maintenance and cleaning work.

TO REDUCE RISKS

- ▼ Ensure that you have chosen a powder coating that presents the lowest risk to your workers' health and safety, and to the environment. Talk to your supplier or trade association for advice. For example, you should only use TGIC-based coating powders when these are needed for technical reasons. Ask your supplier whether you need to use them. Take care when selecting an alternative powder coating as some also contain other hazardous substances such as isocyanates.
- ▼ Minimise the amount of manual spraying carried out - many coating-booths are automatically operated
- ▼ Ensure that your spray booth is working at its optimum so that the air entering the system is at least 0.5 metres per second

- ▼ If using conveyorised spray booths stand outside the booth to spray; do not lean inside
- ▼ Never spray towards another operator
- ▼ The amount of powder sprayed should be kept to the level that minimises its usage and achieves the desired finish, by controlling gun settings
- ▼ Provide suitable personal protective equipment and make sure it is worn properly
- ▼ Train your employees in safe powder coating techniques to minimise exposure
- ▼ Practise good housekeeping by keeping work areas around the spray booths clean. Use an industrial vacuum cleaner rather than sweeping up with a broom
- ▼ Follow safe systems of work for cleaning and maintenance activities; in particular, the use of compressed air for cleaning should be kept to a minimum and operators should avoid standing inside the booth to clean it by using long-handled rubber scrapers (not brushes) and compressed air lances
- ▼ Ensure good standards of personal hygiene by keeping overalls clean by regular washing, and by washing hands before eating and drinking.

> **THE LAW ON THE MAIN HAZARDS ASSOCIATED WITH POWDER COATING** *outlined*
>
> Hazardous substances in coating powders must be controlled in line with the Control of Substances Hazardous to Health Regulations (see page 20).

Other precautions to take include:

- ▼ minimise the risk of a fire or explosion by regular cleaning to prevent build up of dust and exclude sources of ignition, such as naked flames, cigarettes, etc from powder coating work areas
- ▼ minimise the risk of electric shock by ensuring good earthing of work equipment and regular maintenance of electrical equipment
- ▼ maintain compressed air systems associated with powder coating equipment (see page 28)

KEY REFERENCES: *Controlling exposure to coating powders*
HSG203 2000 HSE Books ISBN 0 7176 1761 0
Working safely with coating powders
INDG319 HSE Books 2000 (single copy free or priced packs of 10 ISBN 0 7176 1776 9)

PERSONAL PROTECTIVE EQUIPMENT (PPE)

If you are thinking of using personal protective equipment (PPE) to control employees' exposure to substances hazardous to health remember that COSHH (see page 20) limits its use to situations where it is not reasonably practicable to use other measures.

THE PERSONAL PROTECTIVE EQUIPMENT AT WORK REGULATIONS 1992 *outlined*

Employers must:

■ provide suitable PPE free of charge to protect employees against risks which have not been controlled by other means

■ take all reasonable steps to ensure it is properly used

■ before providing PPE, assess risks to health and safety which have not been avoided by other means and define the characteristics which PPE must have against those risks; then compare those characteristics against PPE available

■ maintain PPE provided in clean and efficient working order with appropriate accommodation for it when not in use

■ give information, instruction and training.

Employees must:

■ use PPE provided

■ report any loss or obvious defect to the employer.

RESPIRATORY PROTECTIVE EQUIPMENT (RPE)

Choosing

When choosing breathing protection consider in detail the job to be done. For example, are the insides or undersides of large articles to be sprayed?

It is likely that the ventilation will be less effective in these areas. Different types of RPE offer different levels of protection and the correct type has to be matched to the job and the wearer. For most spray jobs with the sprayer inside the booth, compressed airline breathing apparatus with a full facepiece or air fed equipment may be most suitable. Before choosing, assess the work carefully and consult your suppliers of paint and protective equipment.

Maintaining

Thoroughly examine and, where appropriate, test RPE at least once a month and more frequently where conditions are severe. (This does not apply to one-shift disposable respirators.) Half-mask respirators used only occasionally against dust or fumes of relatively low toxicity may be examined at longer intervals, but not less than once every three months.

Ensure that breathing air supplied to equipment is satisfactory; proprietary equipment to do this is widely available.

KEY REFERENCES: *Personal Protective Equipment at Work Regulations - Guidance on Regulations* L25   HSE Books ISBN 0 7176 0415 2; *The selection, use and maintenance of respiratory protective equipment* HSG53   HSE Books ISBN 0 7176 1537 5

PERSONAL PROTECTIVE EQUIPMENT (PPE)

EAR PROTECTION

Protectors should:

▼ be suitable for conditions in which they are to be used

▼ Provide sufficient attenuation to reduce the noise exposure level to below 90dB(A) and preferably to below 85dB(A)

▼ only be issued on a personal basis

▼ never be removed in a noisy environment

▼ be compatible with other forms of necessary personal protective equipment.

In relation to ear protection, **THE NOISE AT WORK REGULATIONS 1989** *require in outline*

■ ear protection to be made available on request if the daily noise exposure exceeds 85dB(A)

■ ear protection to be worn if the daily noise exposure exceeds 90dB(A)

EYE PROTECTION

Will have to be provided and used (sometimes throughout the whole workshop) where work which puts eyes at risk is carried out, eg:

▼ machining (particularly grinding) and the use of hand tools which leads to the uncontrolled ejection of metallic particles, and

▼ the use of harmful substances, such as metalworking fluids, paints or solvents which may splash into the eye.

The provision and use of **FOOT PROTECTION** will also have to be considered in most engineering workshops where there are risks of injury to the feet, for example from heavy components being moved.

Where any PPE is needed to help control a risk to health or safety of an employee, it must be provided and maintained (including cleaning of overalls) free of charge to the employee.

KEY REFERENCE: *Protect your hearing or lose it* **INDG363 1999 HSE Books**
(single copy free or priced packs of 25 ISBN 0 7176 2540 0)

OFFICES

ACCIDENTS and cases of **ILL HEALTH** are generally less frequent and severe in offices. To minimise risks:

DO
- clear up spillages
- replace/repair torn floor covering
- also see the general advice on the workplace (see pages 8-10)
- follow legal requirements (see Key References below) for continuous or extensive use of VDUs, ensure adequate breaks and provide workstations which are reasonably adjustable for comfort (see pages 12-17 on how to avoid upper limb disorders).

DON'T
- allow trailing leads to create tripping hazards.

Electricity in offices can cause the most serious accidents from electric shock and fire; defective plugs, sockets and leads cause more accidents than appliances themselves.

DO
- provide enough socket outlets; avoid or minimise the use of adaptors
- test any residual current devices fitted
- visually inspect plugs and leads and get them repaired by someone competent if necessary
- consider whether more detailed tests are needed (for example, is the equipment faulty or only working intermittently?)
- switch off and unplug before cleaning.

DON'T
- use taped joints in electrical cables (see pages 26-27).

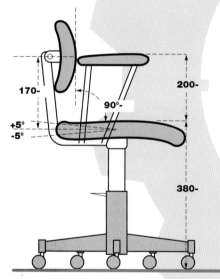

Recommended adjustability

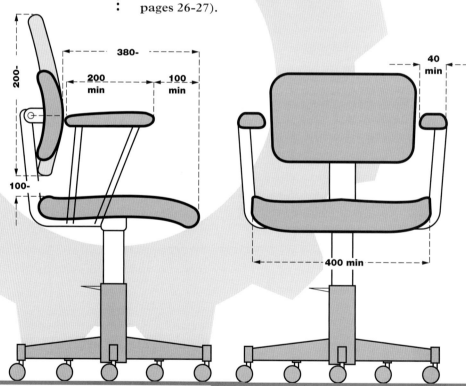

Recommended dimensions

CHAIRS *All dimensions in millimetres*

KEY REFERENCE:
The law on VDUs: An easy guide HSG90 HSE Books ISBN 0 7176 2602 4

ORGANISING HEALTH AND SAFETY

WHAT THE LAW REQUIRES

Under the HSW Act, you have to ensure the health and safety of yourself and others who may be affected by what you do or fail to do. This includes people who: work for you, including casual workers, part-timers, trainees and sub-contractors; use workplaces you provide; are allowed to use your equipment; visit your premises; may be affected by your work, eg your neighbours or the public; use products you make, supply or import; or use your professional services, eg if you also design as well as make machinery,

The Act applies to all work activities and premises, and everyone at work has responsibilities under it, including the self-employed.

BASIC LEGAL REQUIREMENTS *outlined*

You must:

- have a written, up-to-date health and safety policy if you employ five or more people
- carry out a risk assessment (and if you employ five or more people, record the main findings and your arrangements for health and safety)
- notify occupation of premises to your local inspector if you are a commercial or industrial business
- display a current certificate as required by the Employers' Liability (Compulsory Insurance) Act 1969 if you employ anyone
- display the Health and Safety Law poster for employees or give out the leaflet
- notify certain types of injuries, occupational diseases and events
- consult your employees, either directly or via appointed union safety representatives on certain issues, such as any changes which might affect health and safety and any information and training which has to be provided

You must not

- employ children of under school leaving age, apart from on authorised work experience schemes, if you are an industrial undertaking.

ENFORCING THE LAW

Health and safety laws relating to your firm will usually be enforced by a health and safety inspector from the HSE, but where the workshop is part of a larger enterprise, such as a large department store where health and safety law is enforced by the local authority, by a local authority inspector.

Inspectors may visit workplaces without notice but you are entitled to see their identification before they come in. They may want to investigate an accident or complaint, or inspect safety, health and welfare in the workshop. They have the right to talk to employees and safety representatives, take photographs and samples, and even in certain cases to impound dangerous equipment. They are entitled to co-operation and answers to questions.

Inspectors will be aware of the main risks in engineering workshops and will give you help and advice on how to comply with the law. If there is a problem they may issue a formal notice requiring improvements or, where serious danger exists, one which prohibits the use of a process or equipment.

Inspectors have powers to prosecute a firm (or an individual) for breaking health and safety law.

KEY REFERENCE: *Essentials of health and safety at work* HSE Books ISBN 0 7176 0716 X

FIRST AID

A first-aid box should contain a sufficient quantity of suitable first-aid materials and nothing else no lotions, medicines or treatments (including paracetamol).

The box of a typical small workshop with no additional or special hazards may include:

Item	Quantity
Guidance Card IND(G) 4 (P) Rev	1
Individually wrapped sterile adhesive dressings (assorted size)	20
Sterile eye pads, with attachment	2
Individually wrapped triangular bandages	6
Safety pins	6
Medium sized individually wrapped sterile unmedicated wound dressings (approx 10 cm x 8 cm)	6
Large sterile and individually wrapped unmedicated wound dressings (approx 13 cm x 9 cm)	2
Extra large sterile individually wrapped unmedicated wound dressings (approx 28 cm x 17.5 cm)	3

If work in confined spaces, such as large metal fabrications or vapour degreasing tanks is carried out, resuscitating equipment should be provided and maintained, and persons trained in its use.

If cyanide or other especially hazardous substances are used, appropriate antidotes, equipment and training should also be provided, and the suppliers of the substances concerned, or EMAS, consulted in the first instance.

HEALTH AND SAFETY (FIRST AID) REGULATIONS 1981 *outlined*

You must have:

- someone who can take charge in an emergency. (The minimum requirement is for an appointed person to be available whenever people are at work - and is the lowest grade of first aid cover)
- a first-aid box
- notices telling people where the first-aid box is and who the appointed person is
- a qualified first aider where the situation demands, eg if your work gives rise to special hazards, such as those from toxic materials or dangerous machinery
- a first-aid room if you are a long way from emergency medical services.

As your company grows, look again at your need for qualified first aiders. They must be properly trained and have a valid first aid at work certificate. These certificates are issued for three years but can be renewed following refresher training and re-examination. Training organisations are registered with the Employment Medical Advisory Service - ask your Employment Nursing Adviser at the local HSE office.

KEY REFERENCES: *Basic advice on first aid at work* **INDG347**
(single copy free or priced packs of 20 ISBN 0 7176 2261 4)
First aid at work. Approved Code of Practice and Guidance
L74 HSE Books ISBN 0 7176 1050 0

HOW TO OBTAIN PUBLICATIONS AND FURTHER ASSISTANCE

HSE Publications

HSE priced and free publications are available by mail order from HSE Books, PO Box 1999, Sudbury, Suffolk CO10 2WA Tel: 01787 881165 Fax: 01787 313995 Website: www.hsebooks.co.uk (HSE priced publications are also available from bookshops.)

For information about health and safety ring HSE's InfoLine Tel: 08701 545500 Fax: 02920 859260 e-mail: hseinformationservices@natbrit.com or write to HSE Information Services, Caerphilly Business Park, Caerphilly CF83 3GG. You can also visit HSE's website: www.hse.gov.uk

Engineering sector pages:
www.open.gov.uk/hse/fod/engship.htm.

HSC Newsletter is available on subscription from:

HSE Books
Subscriptions Department
PO Box 1999, Sudbury, Suffolk CO10 2WA
Tel: 01787 881165   Fax: 01787 313995

Other sources of information

British Safety Council
National Safety Centre, 70 Chancellors Road
London W6 9RS
Tel: 020 8741 1231   Fax: 020 8741 4555

Royal Society for the Prevention of Accidents
Edgbaston Park, 353 Bristol Road
Birmingham B5 7ST
Tel: 0121 248 2000   Fax: 0121 248 2001

The Manufacturing Technologies Association
62 Bayswater Road, London W2 3PS
Tel: 020 7298 6400   Fax: 020 7298 6430
Website: www.mta.org.uk

Surface Engineering Association
Confederation House
10 Vyse St
Birmingham B18 6LT
Tel: 0121 236 2657   Fax: 0121 237 1124

EEF. The Manufacturers' Organisation
Broadway House, Tothill Street
London SW1H 9NQ
Tel: 020 7222 7777   Fax: 020 7222 2782
Website: www.eef.org.uk

AMICUS AEU
Engineering Section
Terry Duffy House, Thomas Street
Holloway Circus, Queensway
West Bromwich B70 6NT
Tel: 0121 643 1042   Fax: 0121 569 8910

Envirowise
Harwell
Oxfordshire OX11 0RA
Tel: 0800 585794   Fax: 0870 1906713

Other publications

Stationery Office publications are available from:

The Publications Centre
PO Box 276, London SW8 5DT
Tel: 0870 600 5522   Fax: 0870 600 5533
Website: www.tso.co.uk (They are also available from bookshops.)

British Standards are available from:

BSI Customer Services
389 Chiswick High Road London W4 4AL
Tel: 020 8996 9001   Fax: 020 8996 7001
Website: www.bsi-global.com

HSE videos are available from HSE Books

FURTHER READING AND INFORMATION

Unless otherwise indicated, the following titles are available from HSE Books.

Managing health and safety

HSG65	*Successful health and safety management* rev 1997 ISBN 0 7176 1276 7
HSG96	*The costs of accidents at work* rev 1997 ISBN 0 7176 1343 7
L21	*Management of health and safety at work. Management of Health and Safety at Work Regulations 1999. Approved Code of Practice and guidance* (Second edition) HSE Books 2000 ISBN 0 7176 2488 9
INDG324	*Starting your business. Guidance on preparing a health and safety policy document for small firms* (single copy free; ISBN 0 7176 1799 8 for priced pack of 5 copies)
HSC13(rev1)	*Health and safety regulation: a short guide* 2003 (free)
HSE40	*Employers' Liability (Compulsory Insurance) Act 1969* 2002 (free)
HSE34	*HSE and you* 2000 (free)
HSE38	*HSE: Working with employers* 2000 (free)
INDG275	*Management of health and safety. Five steps to success* 1998 (single copy free; ISBN 0 7176 2170 7 for priced packs of 10 copies)
INDG163(rev1)	*5 steps to risk assessment* 1998 (single copies free; ISBN 0 7176 1565 0 for priced packs of 10 copies)
L87	*Safety representatives and safety committees* (Third edition) HSE Books 1996 ISBN 0 7176 1220 1
HSG137	*Health risk management* 1995 ISBN 0 7176 0905 7
–	*Essentials of health and safety at work* 1994 ISBN 0 7176 0716 X
SCB 014	*Be safe: A guide to health and safety in training* available from Department for Education and Skills, tel 0845 6022260
INDG355	*Reduce risks - cut costs: The real cost of accidents and ill health at work* 2002 (single copy free; ISBN 0 7176 2337 8 for priced packs of 15 copies)
INDG322	*Need help on health and safety?* 2000 (single copy free; ISBN 0 7176 1790 4 for priced packs of 10 copies)
HSC14	*What to expect when a health and safety inspector calls* 1998 (free)
INDG232	*Consulting employees on health and safety: A guide to the Law* (single copies free; ISBN 0 7176 1615 0 for priced packs of 15 copies)
INDG218	*Guide to risk assessment requirements: Common provisions in health and safety law* (single copies free; ISBN 0 7176 1211 2 for priced packs of 5 copies)
HSG165	*Young people at work: A guide for employers* (Second edition) 2000 ISBN 0 7176 1889 7
–	*A guide to the Working Time Regulations* DTI tel 08701 502 500
HSG218	*Tackling work-related stress: A manager's guide* 2001 ISBN 0 7176 2050 6
HSG183	*Five steps to risk assessment: Case studies* 1998 ISBN 0 7176 1580 4
L95	*A guide to the Health and Safety (Consultation with Employees) Regulations 1996* 1996 ISBN 0 7176 1234 1
	Improving maintenance: A guide to reducing human error 2000 ISBN 0 7176 1818 8

Workshops

HSG194	*Thermal comfort in the workplace: Guidance for employers* 1999 ISBN 0 7176 2468 4
L64	*Safety signs and signals. The Health and Safety (Safety Signs and Signals) Regulations 1996. Guidance on Regulations* 1996 ISBN 0 7176 0870 0
L24	*Workplace health, safety and welfare. Workplace (Health Safety and Welfare) Regulations 1992. Approved Code of Practice and Guidance* 1992 ISBN 0 7176 0413 6
INDG244	*Workplace health, safety and welfare: A short guide* 1997 (single copies free; ISBN 0 7176 1328 3 for priced packs of 10 copies)
HSG38	*Lighting at work* 1998 ISBN 0 7176 1232 5
INDG63(rev)	*Passive smoking at work: Workplace air pollution* 1992 (single copies free; ISBN 0 7176 0882 4 for priced packs of 10 copies)
INDG225	*Preventing slips, trips and falls* (single copies free; ISBN 0 7176 1183 3 for priced packs of 15 copies)
INDG36(rev2)	*Working with VDUs* (single copies free; ISBN 0 7176 2222 3 for priced packs of 10 copies)
HSG165	*Young people at work: A guide for employers* (Second edition) 2000 ISBN 0 7176 1889 7
HSG122	*New and expectant mothers at work: A guide for employers* (Second edition) 2002 ISBN 0 7176 2583 4
HSG155	*Slip and trips. Guidance for employers on identifying hazards and controlling risks* 1996 ISBN 0 7176 1145 0

Lifting equipment

L113	*Safe use of lifting equipment. Lifting Operations and Lifting Equipment Regulations. Approved Code of Practice and guidance* 1998 ISBN 0 7176 1628 2
PM55	*Safe working with overhead travelling cranes* 1985 ISBN 0 11 883524 6

Manual handling

L23	*Manual handling. Manual Handling Operations Regulations 1992. Guidance on Regulations* (Second edition) 1998 ISBN 0 7176 2415 3
INDG90(rev2)	*Understanding ergonomics at work: Reduce accidents and ill health and increase productivity by fitting the task to the worker* 2003 (single copies free; ISBN 0 7176 2599 0 for priced packs of 15 copies)
INDG143(rev1)	*Getting to grips with manual handling: A short guide for employers* 2000 (single copies free); ISBN 0 7176 1754 8 for priced packs of 15 copies
INDG171	*Aching arms (or RSI) in small businesses: Is ill health due to upper limb disorders a problem in your workplace?* 2003 (single copies free; ISBN 0 7176 2600 8 for priced packs of 15 copies)
HSG60	*Upper limb disorders: A guide to prevention* (rev) 2002 ISBN 0 7176 1978 8
HSG57	*Seating at work* 1998 ISBN 0 7176 1231 7
HSG115	*Manual handling: Solutions you can handle* 1994 ISBN 0 7176 0693 7
HSG121	*A pain in your workplace? Ergonomic problems and solutions* 1994 ISBN 0 7176 0668 6
EIS16	*Preventing injuries from the manual handling of sharp edges in the engineering industry* (free)
INDG390	*Choosing a welding set? Make sure you can handle it* 2003 (single copy free; ISBN 0 7176 2773 X for priced packs of 10 copies)

Transport (and storage)

L117	*Rider operated lift trucks - operator training. Approved Code of Practice and guidance* 1999 ISBN 0 7176 2455 2
HSG6	*Safety in working with lift trucks* 2000 ISBN 0 7176 1781 5
INDG148	*Reversing vehicles* 1993 (single copies free; ISBN 0 7176 1063 2 for priced packs of 15 copies)
HSG76	*Health and safety in retail and wholesale warehouses* 1992 ISBN 0 7176 0445 4
HSG136	*Workplace transport safety* 1995 ISBN 0 7176 0935 9
INDG199	*Managing vehicle safety at the workplace* 1995 (single copies free; ISBN 0 7176 0982 0 for priced packs of 10 copies)
INDG313	*Safe unloading of steel stock* 2000 (single copies free or priced packs of 15 ISBN 0 7176 1765 3)

Hazardous substances

L132	*Control of lead at work. Control of Lead at Work Regulations 2002. Approved Code of Practice and guidance* (Third edition) HSE Books 2002 ISBN 0 7176 2565 6
EH40/2002	*Occupational exposure limits* ISBN 0 7176 2083 2 Supplement 2003 ISBN 0 7176 2172 3
HSG37	*An introduction to local exhaust ventilation* 1993 ISBN 0 7176 1001 2
HSG54	*The maintenance, examination and testing of local exhaust ventilation* 1998 ISBN 0 7176 1485 9
INDG174	*A short guide to the Personal Protective Equipment at Work Regulations 1992* (single copies free; ISBN 0 7176 0889 1 for priced packs of 10 copies)
INDG233	*Preventing dermatitis at work* (single copies free; ISBN 0 7176 1553 7 for priced packs of 15 copies)
INDG95(rev2)	*Respiratory sensitisers and COSHH* (single copies free; ISBN 0 7176 0914 6 for priced packs of 15 copies)
INDG188	*Asbestos alert for building maintenance, repair and refurbishment workers* (pocket card) 1995 (single copies free; ISBN 0 7176 1209 0 for priced packs of 25 copies)
INDG223(rev1)	*Managing asbestos in workplace buildings* 1996 (single copies free; ISBN 0 7176 1179 5 for priced packs of 10 copies)
INDG136(rev2)	*COSHH: A brief guide to the Regulations* (single copies free; ISBN 0 7176 2677 6 for priced packs of 10 copies)
HSG126	*CHIP for everyone* 2002 ISBN 0 7176 2370 X
L5	*Control of substances hazardous to health. The Control of Substances Hazardous to Health Regulations 2002. Approved Code of Practice and guidance* (Fourth edition) HSE Books 2002 ISBN 0 7176 2534 6
L8	*Legionnaires' disease. The control of legionella bacteria in water systems. Approved Code of Practice and guidance* (Second edition) HSE Books 2002 ISBN 0 7176 1772 6
INDG181	*The idiot's guide to CHIP 3* 2002 (single copies free; ISBN 0 7176 2333 5 for priced packs of 5 copies)
HSG53	*The selection, use and maintenance of respiratory protective equipment: A practical guide* rev 1998 ISBN 0 7176 1537 5
L25	*Personal protective equipment at work. Personal Protective Equipment at Work Regulations 1992. Guidance on Regulations* HSE Books 1992 ISBN 0 7176 0415 2

MS25   *Medical aspects of occupational asthma* rev 1998 ISBN 0 7176 1547 2

L55   *Preventing asthma at work: How to control respiratory sensitisers*
HSE Books 1994 ISBN 0 7176 0661 9

HSG61   *Surveillance of people exposed to health risks at work* 1999 ISBN 0 7176 1705 X

EH1   *Cadmium: health and safety precautions* 1995 ISBN 0 7176 0825 5

EH13   *Beryllium: health and safety precautions* 1995 ISBN 0 7176 0824 7

EH60   *Nickel and its inorganic compounds: Health and safety precautions* 1997
ISBN 0 7176 1341 0

HSG193   *COSHH essentials: Easy steps to control chemicals. Control of Substances
Hazardous to Health Regulations* (Second edition) 2003 ISBN 0 7176 2737 3 It
can also be freely accessed at www.coshh-essentials.org.uk

HSG188   *Health risk management: A guide to working with solvents* 1999
ISBN 0 7176 1664 9

HSG110   *Seven steps to successful substitution of hazardous substances* 1994
ISBN 0 7176 0695 3

HSG173   *Monitoring strategies for toxic substances* 1997 ISBN 0 7176 1411 5

HSG203   *Controlling exposure to coating powders* HSG203 2000 ISBN 0 7176 1761 0

INDG319   *Working safely with coating powders* 2000 (single copy free or priced packs of
10 ISBN 0 7176 1776 9)

Electricity

HSR25   *Memorandum of guidance on The Electricity at Work Regulations 1989,*
1989 ISBN 0 7176 1602 9

HSG85   *Electricity at work: Safe working practices* 2003 ISBN 0 7176 2164 2

HSG107   *Maintaining portable and transportable electrical equipment* 1994
ISBN 0 7176 0715 1

BS 7671:2001   *Requirements for electrical installations. IEE Wiring Regulations*
ISBN 0 85296 9880

GS38   *Electrical test equipment for use by electricians* 1995 ISBN 0 7176 0845 X

INDG231   *Electrical safety and you* (single copies free; ISBN 0 7176 1207 4 for priced packs
of 15 copies)

PM29   *Electrical hazards from steam/water pressure cleaners* 1995 ISBN 0 7176 0813 1

INDG68   *Do you use a steam/water pressure cleaner? You could be in for a shock* 1997
(free)

INDG354   *Safety in electrical testing at work: General guidance* 2002 (single copy free or
priced packs of 5 ISBN 0 7176 2296 7)

Pressurised plant and systems

L122   *Safety of pressure systems. Pressure Systems Safety Regulations 2000. Approved
Code of Practice.* HSE Books 2000 ISBN 0 7176 1767 X

GS 4   *Safety in pressure testing* 1998 ISBN 0 7176 1629 0

PM60   *Steam boiler blowdown systems* rev 1998 ISBN 0 7176 1533 2

HSG39   *Compressed air safety* rev 1998 ISBN 0 7176 1531 6

Machinery safeguarding

–   *Product standards: Machinery - guidance notes on UK regulations* Ref 95650 (free)
Department of Trade and Industry, tel: 0870 1502500

SI 1992/3073   *Supply of Machinery (Safety) Regulations 1992* (as amended by SI 1994/2063)

L22	*Safe use of work equipment. Provision and Use of Work Equipment Regulations 1998 Approved Code of Practice and guidance* 1998 ISBN 0 7176 1626 6
EIS12	*Safety at manually-fed pivoting-head metal-cutting circular saws* 1998 (free)
EIS7	*Safeguarding 3 roll bending machines* 1998 (free)
EIS13	*Safeguarding of combination metalworking machines* 2000 (free)
EIS33	*CNC turning machines: Controlling risks from ejected parts* 2001 (free)
EIS2	*Accidents at metalworking lathes using emery cloth* 1993 (free)
PM83	*Drilling machines: guarding of spindles and attachments* 1998 ISBN 0 7176 1546 4
L112	*Safe use of power presses. Provision and Use of Work Equipment Regulations 1998 as applied to power presses. Approved Code of Practice and guidance* 1998 ISBN 0 7176 1627 4
HSG17	*Safety in the use of abrasive wheels* 2000 ISBN 0 7176 1739 4
HSG42	*Safety in the use of metal cutting guillotines and shears* 1988 ISBN 0 11 885455 0
HSG43	*Industrial robot safety: Your guide to the safeguarding of industrial robots* 2000 ISBN 0 7176 1310 0
BS EN 60825	*Safety of laser products.* Part 1: 1994 *Equipment classification, requirements and user's guide*
IEC 60825-1:1993	*Safety of laser products* (including 1997 and 2001 amendments)
EIS19	*Engineering machine tools: retrofitting CNC* 1997 (free)
EIS28	*Safeguarding at horizontal boring machines* 1998 (free)
HSG236	*Power presses: Maintenance and thorough examination* 2003 ISBN 0 7176 2171 5
HSG180	*Application of electro-sensitive protective equipment using light curtains and light beam devices in machinery* 1999 ISBN 0 7176 1550 2
Video	*Power presses Parts 1 and 2* 1992 ISBN 0 7176 1994 X

Metalworking fluids

INDG365	*Working safely with metalworking fluids* 2003 (single copy free; ISBN 0 7176 2545 1 for priced packs of 10 copies)
–	*Exposure to hard metals in metalworking fluids during machining operations* British Lubricants Federation 1994, available from BLF, tel: 01442 230589
Video package	*Metalworking fluids: Effective coolant care and the control of risks to health* 1994 ISBN 0 7176 0875 1
Pack	*Working safely with metalworking fluids* 2002 ISBN 0 7176 2561 3

Noise

L108	*Reducing noise at work. Guidance on the Noise at Work Regulations 1989* 1998 ISBN 0 7176 1511 1
INDG362	*Noise at work: Advice for employers* (single copy free; ISBN 0 7176 2539 7 for priced packs of 10 copies)
INDG363	*Protect your hearing or lose it!* 2002 (single copy free; ISBN 0 7176 2540 0 for priced packs of 25 copies)

HSG138	*Sound solutions: Techniques to reduce noise at work* 1995 ISBN 0 7176 0791 7
INDG201	*Protect your hearing or lose it* (single copies free; ISBN 0 7176 2540 5 for priced packs of 25 copies)
PM56	*Noise from pneumatic systems* 1985 ISBN 0 11 883529 7
INDG362 (rev)	*Noise at work. Advice for employers* 1995 (single copies free; ISBN 0 7176 2539 7 for priced packs of 10 copies)
EIS26	*Noise in engineering* 1998 (free)
EIS29	*Control of noise at power presses* 1998 (free)

Vibration

INDG126(rev1)	*Health risks from hand-arm vibration: Advice for employees and the self-employed* 1998 (single copies free; ISBN 0 7176 1554 5 for priced packs of 15 copies)
INDG175	*Health risks from hand-arm vibration: Advice for employers* rev 1998 (single copies free; ISBN 0 7176 1553 7 for priced packs of 10 copies).
HSG88	*Hand-arm vibration* 1994 ISBN 0 7176 0743 7
HSG170	*Vibration solutions* 1997 ISBN 0 7176 0954 5
INDG338	*Power tools: How to reduce health risks. Guide for employers* (single copy free or priced packs of 15 ISBN 0 7176 2008 5)

Cleaning and degreasing

INDG98	*Permit-to-work systems* 1991 (single copies free; ISBN 0 7176 1331 3 for priced packs of 15 copies)
L101	*Safe work in confined spaces. Confined Spaces Regulations 1997. Approved Code of Practice, Regulations and guidance* ISBN 0 7176 1405 0
EIS20(rev1)	*Maintenance and cleaning of solvent degreasing tanks* 1998 (free)
EIS21	*Immersion and cold cleaning of engineering components* (free)
GG354	*Surface cleaning and preparation: Choosing the best option* Envirowise (see page 61)
EIS40	*Safe use of solvent degreasing plant* 2003 (free)
EIS34	*Surface cleaning: Solvent update including the reclassification of trichloroethylene* 2002 (free)

Flamecutting and welding

HSG118	*Electrical safety in arc welding* 1994 ISBN 0 7176 0704 6
HSE8	*Oxygen: Fire and explosion hazards in the use and misuse of oxygen* 1992 (free)
CS15	*Cleaning and gas freeing of tanks containing flammable residues* 1985 ISBN 0 7176 1365 8
–	*Health and safety in welding and allied processes* (4th Ed) N.Balchin, Welding Institute 2002 ISBN 0 85573 538 5 (available from Woodhead Publishing, tel: 01223 891358)
–	*Welding fume: A welder's guide* 1985 Welding Institute (available from Woodhead Publishing, Tel: 01223 891358)
BS EN ISO 10882-1: 2001	*Health and safety in welding and allied processes. Sampling of airborne particles and gases in the operator's breathing zone* British Standards Institution
BS EN 169: 2002	*Personal eye-protection. Filters for welding and related techniques* British Standards Institution
BS EN 166: 2002	*Personal eye-protection. Specifications* British Standards Institution

BS EN 175: 1997   *Personal protection. Equipment for eye and face protection during welding and allied processes* British Standards Institution

HSG139   *The safe use of compressed gases in welding, flame cutting and allied processes* 1997 ISBN 0 7176 0680 5

HSG204   *Health and safety in arc welding* 2000 ISBN 0 7176 1813 7

INDG327   *Take care with acetylene* 2000 (single copy free or priced packs of 10 ISBN 0 7176 1817 X)

Radiography

L121   *Work with ionising radiation. Ionising Radiations Regulations 1999. Approved Code of Practice and guidance.* HSE Books 2000 ISBN 0 7176 1746 7

IRIS1(rev1)   *Industrial radiography: Managing radiation risks* 2000 (free)

IRIS2(rev1)   *Radiation doses: Assessment and recording* 2000 (free)

–   *Radiation safety for site radiography* Engineering Construction Industry Association tel: 0171 799 2000 ISBN 0 903393 867 (o/p; updated version due 2004)

Painting

HSG51   *Storage of flammable liquids in containers* (rev 1998) ISBN 0 7176 1471 9

HSG140   *Safe use and handling of flammable liquids* 1996 ISBN 0 7176 0967 7

EH16   *Isocyanates: Health hazards and precautionary measures* 1999 ISBN 0 7176 1701 7

–   *Code of safe practice: Application of thermosetting coating powders by electrostatic spraying* 1997 available from the British Coating Federation, tel: 01372 360660

SI 2002/2776   *The Dangerous Substances and Explosive Atmospheres Regulations 2002* The Stationery Office ISBN 0 11 042957 5

INDG227   *Safe working with flammable substances* (single copies free; ISBN 0 7176 1154 X for priced packs of 15 copies)

EIS15   *Control of exposure to triglycidyl isocyanurate (TGIC) in powder coatings* 1998 (free)

HSG178   *The spraying of flammable liquids* 1998 ISBN 0 7176 1483 2

Offices

INDG236   *Maintaining portable electrical equipment in offices and other low risk environments* (single copies free; ISBN 0 7176 1272 4 for priced packs of 10 copies)

INDG36(rev1)   *Working with VDUs* 1998 (single copies free; ISBN 0 7176 1504 9 for priced packs of 10 copies)

L26   *Work with display screen equipment. Health and Safety (Display Screen Equipment) Regulations* 1992 *as amended by the Health and Safety (Miscellaneous Amendments) Regulations 2002. Guidance on Regulations* (Second edition) HSE Books 2003 ISBN 0 7176 2582 6

INDG173   *Officewise* 1994 (single copies free; ISBN 0 7176 0773 9 for priced packs of 10 copies)

HSG90   *The law on VDUs: An easy guide. Make sure your office complies with the Health and Safety (Display Screen Equipment) Regulations 1992 (as amended 2002)* 2003 ISBN 0 7176 2602 4

Accidents and emergencies

L74   *First aid at work. Health and Safety (First Aid) Regulations 1981. Approved Code of Practice and guidance* 1997 ISBN 0 7176 1050 0

Form F2508/   *Report of an injury or dangerous occurrence or case of disease* 1996
FormF2508A   ISBN 0 7176 1078 0

L73   *Guide to the Reporting of Injuries, Diseases and Dangerous Occurrences Regulations 1999* 1999 ISBN 0 7176 2431 5

HSE31(rev1)   *RIDDOR explained* 1999 (single copies free; ISBN 0 7176 2441 2 for priced packs of 10 copies)

INDG214   *First aid at work – your questions answered* 1997 (single copies free; ISBN 0 7176 1074 8 for priced packs of 15 copies)

INDG215   *Basic advice on first aid at work* 2002 (single copies free; ISBN 0 7176 2261 4 for priced packs of 20 copies)

While every effort has been made to ensure the accuracy of the references listed in this publication, their future availability cannot be guaranteed.

HSE OFFICES

South West
Inter City House
Mitchell Lane, Victoria Street
Bristol BS1 6AN Tel: 0117 988 6000

South
Priestley House, Priestley Road
Basingstoke RG24 9NW
Tel: 01256 404000

South East
Phoenix House
23-25 Cantelupe Road, East Grinstead
West Sussex RH19 3BE
Tel: 01342 334200

East Anglia
Wren House
Hedgerows Business Park,
Colchester Road, Springfield, Chelmsford,
Essex CM2 5PF Tel: 01245 706200

Northern Home Counties
14 Cardiff Road, Luton, Beds LU1 1PP
Tel: 01582 444200

East Midlands
5th Floor, Belgrave House, 1 Greyfriars
Northampton NN1 2BS Tel: 01604 738300

West Midlands
1 Hagley Road, Edgbaston
Birmingham B16 8HS
Tel: 0121 607 6200

Wales
Government Buildings
Phase 1, Ty Glas
Llanishen
Cardiff CF14 5SH
Tel: 029 2026 3000

Marches
The Marches House, Midway
Newcastle under Lyme, Staffs ST5 1DT
Tel: 01782 602300

North Midlands
The Pearson Building, 55 Upper
Parliament Street,
Nottingham NG1 6AU Tel: 01159 712800

South Yorkshire & Humberside
Edgar Allen House,
241 Glossop Road,
Sheffield S10 2GW Tel: 0114 291 2300

West & North Yorkshire
Marshall's Mill, Marshall Street,
Leeds LS11 9YJ
Tel: 0113 283 4200

Greater Manchester
Grove House, Skerton Road,
Manchester M16 0RB Tel: 0161 952 8200

North West
Marshall House, Ringway
Preston PR1 2HS Tel: 0161 952 8200

North East
Arden House, Regent Centre
Gosforth, Newcastle upon Tyne NE3 3JN
Tel: 0191 202 6200

Scotland East
Belford House, 59 Belford Road
Edinburgh EH4 3UE Tel: 0131 247 2000

Scotland West
375 West George Street, Glasgow G2 4LW
Tel: 0141 275 3000

(See www.hse.gov.uk/contact/local.htm for up-to-date list of HSE local offices)

SOME USEFUL ADDRESSES FOR SELECTING A HEALTH AND SAFETY CONSULTANCY

Association of Consulting Engineers
Alliance House, 12 Caxton Street
London SW1H OQL

Association of Noise Consultants
6 Trap Road, Guiden Morden, Herts SG8 OJE

British Occupational Hygiene Society
Georgian House, Great Northern Road
Derby DE1 1LT

British Safety Council
Chancellors Road, London W6 9RS

Chartered Institute of Building Services Engineers
Delta House, 222 Balham High Road
London SW12 9BS

Council of Independent Inspecting Authorities
14 St Mary's Parsonage, Manchester M60 9AP

EEF. The Manufacturers' Organisation
Broadway House, Tothill Street
London SW1H 9NQ

The Engineering Society
Devonshire House, Devonshire Square
Loughborough, Leics LE11 3DW

Independent Safety Consultants Association
c/o Hinton and Higgs, The Firs
Marcham Road, Abingdon, Oxon OX14 1AA

The Institute of Acoustics
PO Box 320, St Albans, Herts AL1 19Z

The Institute of Chemical Engineers
165-171 Railway Terrace, Rugby,
Warwicks CV21 3HQ

The Institution of Electrical Engineers
Savoy Place, London WC2R OBL

The Institute of Environmental Health Officers
Chadwick House, Rushworth Street
London SE1 OQT

British Institute of Non-Destructive Testing
1 Spencer Parade, Northampton NN1 5AA

The Institution of Mechanical Engineers
1 Birdcage Walk, London SW1 9JJ

The Institute of Occupational Hygienists
Georgian House, Great Northern Road
Derby DE1 1LT

The Institute of Occupational Safety & Health
The Grange, Highfield Drive
Wigston, Leics LE18 1NN

The Institute of Radiation Protection
64 Dalkeith Road, Harpenden, Herts AL5 5PW

The Royal College of Nursing
Society of Occupational Health Nursing
RCN North Western Area, 18 Fox Street
Preston, Lancs PR1 2AB

The Royal Environmental Health Institute of Scotland
3 Manor Place, Edinburgh EH3 7DH

The Royal Society of Chemistry
Burlington House, Piccadilly, London W1V OBN

The Royal Society for the Prevention of Accidents
Edgbaston Park, 353 Bristol Road, The Priory,
Queensway, Birmingham B5 7ST

The Society of Occupational Medicine
6 St Andrew's Place, Regents Park
London NW1 4LB

The Society for Radiological Protection
148 Buckingham Palace Road
London SW1W 9TR

National Certification Scheme for In-Service Inspection Bodies (NCSIIB)
1 Birdcage Walk, Westminster
London SW1H 9JJ

KEY REFERENCE: *Need help on health and safety?* INDG322 HSE Books (single copies free; ISBN 0 7176 1790 4 for priced packs of 15)

APPENDIX 1

LIFTING CHECKLIST - *SECTION A*

SUMMARY OF ASSESSMENT

Operations covered by this assessment:

Overall priority for remedial action: *Nil/Low/Med/High*

Remedial action to be taken:

Locations:

Personnel involved:

Date by which action is to be taken:

Date for reassessment:

Assessor's name:

Date of assessment:

Signature:

Section A - *Preliminary*:

Q1 Do the operations involve a significant risk of injury?   **Yes / No**

If 'Yes' go to **Q2**. If 'No' the assessment need go no further.

If in doubt answer 'Yes'

Q2 Can the operations be avoided/mechanised/automated at reasonable cost?   **Yes / No**

If 'No' go to **Q3**. If 'Yes' proceed and then check that the result is satisfactory.

Q3*Are the operations clearly within the numerical guidelines for assessment contained in the guidance on the Manual Handling Regulations (pages 42–45)?   **Yes / No**

If 'No' go to Section B. If 'Yes' you may go straight to Section C if you wish.

*This question can only be answered by using pages 42-45 of the publication referenced below:

Section C - *Overall assessment of risk*:

Q   What is your overall assessment of the risk of injury?   **Insignificant/Low/Med/High**

If not '**Insignificant**' go to Section D.

If '**Insignificant**' the assessment need go no further.

Section D - *Remedial action*:

Q   What remedial action should be taken, in order of priority?

i...

ii..

iii...

iv...

v..

And finally:

▼ complete the **SUMMARY** above

▼ compare it with your other manual handling assessments

▼ decide your priorities for action

▼ TAKE ACTION...............*AND CHECK THAT IT HAS THE DESIRED EFFECT*

KEY REFERENCE: *Manual Handling Operations Regulations* 1992. **Guidance on Regulations L23 (Second edition) HSE Books   ISBN 0 7176 2415 3**

LIFTING CHECKLIST - *SECTION B*

Section B - *More detailed assessment, where necessary:*

Questions to consider: (If the answer to a question is 'Yes' place a tick against it and then consider the level of risk)	Level of risk: (Tick as appropriate)				Possible remedial action: (Make rough notes in this column in preparation for completing Section D)
	Yes	Low	Med	High	
The tasks - *do they involve:*					
▼ holding loads away from the trunk?					
▼ twisting?					
▼ stooping?					
▼ reaching upwards?					
▼ large vertical movement?					
▼ long carrying distances?					
▼ strenuous pushing or pulling?					
▼ unpredictable movement of loads?					
▼ repetitive handling?					
▼ insufficient rest or recovery?					
▼ a work-rate imposed by a process?					
The loads - *are they:*					
▼ heavy?					
▼ bulky/unwieldy?					
▼ difficult to grasp?					
▼ unstable/unpredictable?					
▼ intrinsically harmful (eg sharp/hot)?					
The working environment - *are there:*					
▼ constraints on posture?					
▼ poor floors?					
▼ variations in levels?					
▼ hot/cold/humid conditions?					
▼ strong air movements?					
▼ poor lighting conditions?					
Individual capability - *does the job:*					
▼ require unusual capability?					
▼ pose a risk to those with a health problem?					
▼ pose a risk to those who are pregnant?					
▼ call for special information/training?					
Other factors					
Is movement or posture hindered by clothing or personal protective equipment?					

Deciding the level of risk will inevitably call for judgement.

When you have completed Section B go to Section C.

CHECKING WHETHER HANDLING PROBLEMS ARE CAUSING UPPER LIMB DISORDERS

Company/Department:

Workstation: Completed by:

Task:

Worker: Date:

Risk factor	Tick your answer		Action required
	NO	YES	
Does your job involve a lot of:			
FREQUENT — gripping (a tool or workpiece)?			If you have no ticks in the 'YES' column on this page, you are unlikely to have any handling problems caused by work. You need not go on to the following questions.
or — squeezing (eg tool handles)?			
FORCEFUL — twisting?			
or — reaching?			
AWKWARD — moving things (pushing, pulling, lifting)?			However, if you have any ticks in the 'YES' column on this page, there may be a risk in your workplace. You should go on to do the full risk assessment.
finger/hand movement (eg keyboard work)?			
Are there any warning signs of hand/shoulder/ neck problems? For example:			
▼ Actual cases in this or similar work?			
▼ Complaints by workers, eg aches and pains in hands, wrists, arms, shoulders etc? Ask your employees if they have any of these symptoms.			
▼ Home-made, improvised changes to work-stations or tools (eg handles cushioned or made longer)?			

CHECKING WHETHER HANDLING PROBLEMS ARE CAUSING UPPER LIMB DISORDERS

RISK FACTOR	Is risk present?	
	NO	**YES**
FULL RISK ASSESSMENT Are there any factors in the job that make ULDs *likely*, such as:		
Need for a lot of force - *Does the job involve:*		
▼ strong force at the same time as awkward movements or posture, eg bent wrists, work with arms raised or fully extended?		
▼ forceful use of hand/forearm muscles?		
▼ trying to make do with ill-fitting components by forcing them into place?		
▼ tools not ideal for repetitive or frequent use - particularly if squeezing, twisting, or hammering actions are required?		
▼ using equipment designed for a larger or stronger person (eg women using tools designed for men)?		
Rapid, awkward or frequent movement - *Does the job involve:*		
▼ machine pacing, eg to keep up with conveyor?		
▼ frequent repetition of the same small number of movements?		
▼ awkward movements such as twisting or rotation of wrist, movement of wrist from side to side, very bent fingers and wrist, or hand or arm movements beyond a comfortable range?		
▼ pressures on employees to work fast, eg from piecework or bonus systems?		

POSSIBLE SOLUTIONS	RECOMMENDATION FOR ACTION	Tick when action taken
Redesign workstations, eg: ▼ Reposition supply of components to reduce reaching required. ▼ Move controls to more convenient position.		
Redesign job, workstation, and/or tools to avoid over-use of the hand or forearm. Maintain tools, eg keep them sharp and lubricated, for ease of use.		
Improve quality of components, or provide suitable tools for fitting them.		
Replace domestic or DIY hand tools with tools designed for repetitive industrial use. Redesign tool handles to achieve even distribution of force across hand (power grip preferable to pinch grip) and straight rather than bent wrists. Consider replacing hand tools with power tools. Reduce squeezing forces by using weaker springs to triggers etc.		
Redesign equipment or tool (eg counter-balancing to reduce force required). Provide powered version.		
Self pacing is preferable.		
Replan work, eg to break up pause/repetition cycles or spread movement across both hands. Consider adding extra activities to job, to give variety. Consider scope for automation or use of power tools.		
Redesign workstation, controls or shape of tool handles.		
Consider need for such systems (but employees may resist change). Better training in risks may help.		

RISK FACTOR	Is risk present?	
	NO	YES
Awkward or static posture - *Does the job involve:*		
▼ cramped body position, and/or not enough space to change posture?		
▼ arms stretched or overhead for long periods?		
▼ work at awkwardly high or low height (crouching, stooping, or reaching up)?		
Work for long periods without breaks or changes of activity - *Does the job involve:*		
▼ no changes to work routine or variation of tasks?		
▼ no breaks or infrequent breaks?		
▼ worker not able to have short pauses when desired?		
No special arrangements for new employees (or those returning to work after a long break) **- *Does the job involve:***		
▼ people having to work at full pace as soon as they start (or resume) the job?		
▼ no training in risks and ways employees can reduce risks?		
Poor environmental conditions - *Is work carried out:*		
▼ in dim light, shadow or flickering light?		
▼ in cold or otherwise adverse conditions?		
▼ with tools that vibrate?		

POSSIBLE SOLUTIONS	RECOMMENDATION FOR ACTION	Tick when action taken
Improve space available to worker. Provide adjustable workstation (especially chair) for workers who are above or below average height or shape.		
Move materials or controls to more convenient position.		
Move materials or controls to more convenient position.		
If possible, vary tasks to provide changes in activity. If not, check there are adequate rest breaks.		
Check that breaks are taken, especially if work involves continuous effort such as holding tools, or rapidly repeated movements (eg typing).		
Redesign work to make short pauses possible.		
Allow recruits to build up their work rate sensibly as they gain experience.		
Provide training in skills, posture, and warning symptoms for all those at risk.		
Provide better lighting so that workers do not have to adopt awkward postures to see properly.		
Cold (eg in handling frozen foods) may increase the risk. If it is not possible to warm the working environment, check that protective clothing is well designed and does not affect posture or grip.		
Consider whether the job can be done another way to avoid need for high-vibration tools. Or provide vibration-absorbing grip and minimise vibration by proper maintenance.		

APPENDIX 2

METALWORKING FLUIDS QUESTIONNAIRES

QUESTIONNAIRE FOR DETECTION
OF SKIN ABNORMALITIES

To be completed by the employee

NAME: ....

DATE: ....

DATE OF BIRTH: ....

JOB TITLE: ....

COMPANY: ....

1. Since your last review or in the last 12 months have you had any of the following symptoms?

    (a) *redness and swelling of fingers or hands;*   Yes ☐ No ☐

    (b) *cracking of skin on fingers or hands;*   Yes ☐ No ☐

    (c) *blisters on fingers or hands;*   Yes ☐ No ☐

    (d) *flaking or scaling of skin on fingers or hands;*   Yes ☐ No ☐

    (e) *itching of fingers or hands with skin cracks or splits;*   Yes ☐ No ☐

    (f) *spots, redness, swelling of any other part;*   Yes ☐ No ☐

2. Did these problems last for more than three weeks?   Yes ☐ No ☐

3. Did these problems occur more than once?   Yes ☐ No ☐

4. Does your skin get better with periods off work?   Yes ☐ No ☐

5. Have you lost time from work with skin problems since your last assessment?   Yes ☐ No ☐

6. Do you think you know what causes the problems?   Yes ☐ No ☐

7. Name the substance/material/contact you think is responsible:

To be completed by the responsible person:

8. Problems confirmed by the responsible person?   Yes ☐ No ☐

9. Action taken:

    Name of responsible person:

    Date:

Footnote: Any abnormalities found should be referred to the works occupational health physician or nurse if there is one. If not, employees should be advised to consult their general practitioner. In either case, referral to a consultant dermatologist may be appropriate. A copy of this completed questionnaire should be supplied to the employee's general practitioner.

QUESTIONNAIRE FOR DETECTION
OF LUNG PROBLEMS

To be completed by the employee

NAME: ....

DATE: ....

DATE OF BIRTH: ....

JOB TITLE: ....

COMPANY: ....

Since your last review or in the last 12 months:

1.   Have you had any episodes of wheezes or chest tightness?   Yes ☐   No ☐
     If 'yes', at what time(s) of day?

2.   Have you taken any treatment for your chest?   Yes ☐   No ☐

3.   Have you woken at night with cough or chestiness?   Yes ☐   No ☐

4.   Have you had any episodes of breathlessness?   Yes ☐   No ☐
     If 'yes', at what time(s) of day?

5.   Have you had any time off work with chest disease?   Yes ☐   No ☐

6.   Have you developed chest tightness or breathlessness after exercise?   Yes ☐   No ☐

7.   Have you developed difficulty with breathing?   Yes ☐   No ☐
     If 'yes', at what time(s) of day?

To be completed by the responsible person:

8.   Problems confirmed by the responsible person?   Yes ☐   No ☐

9.   Action taken:

     Name of responsible person:
     Date:

Footnote: If the answer is yes to any of these questions, the employee should be referred to the works occupational health physician or nurse if there is one. If not, employees should be advised to consult their general practitioner. In either case, referral to a consultant chest physician may be appropriate. A copy of this completed questionnaire should be supplied to the employee's general practitioner.

APPENDIX 3

WORK EQUIPMENT RISK ASSESSMENT

You may wish to use the proforma below to assess aspects of machinery safety as part of your risk assessment. Where further action is indicated, you should record what is done as a result. Don't forget to make sure that you also consider fully any risks to health that may arise as a consequence of using the equipment being assessed. For mobile work equipment, additional requirements will apply (see page 19)

General equipment description

DESCRIPTION: ....

LOCATION: .... PLANT/REF No:......................................

NAME OF ASSESSOR: .... DATE OF ASSESSMENT:........................

General description of work equipment, including details of ancillary equipment where relevant:

Intended function of work equipment:

Assessment of suitability for intended function:

Work equipment risk assessment

1 **Guarding of dangerous parts.**

Is access possible to any part of machinery that could cause injury?

Machine part	Location	Part of body at risk	Estimated injury

For the parts identified above, what method of safeguarding is necessary to minimise the risk?

Machine part	Fixed guard	Other guard	Other (jigs, holders etc)

Where guards are currently provided, do they satisfy the following criteria? (Y/N)

Guard/device	Suitable?	Of good construction	Easily by-passed or disabled?	Adequate distance from danger?	Adequate view (if needed)?	Access only for maintenance?

2 Maintenance

What maintenance is needed for guards and protection devices?

Guards/protection device	Maintenance required	Frequency

3 Inspection

Is inspection of the work equipment necessary?

Inspection required (Y/N)	Details of inspection	Frequency

4 Information, instruction and training

What information, instruction and training must be provided for the following groups?

Operators	Maintenance staff	Managers/supervisors

5 Other hazards

What action is needed in respect of the following possible additional hazards?

NOTE: The list in the table below is not exhaustive and is intended as a GUIDE ONLY

Hazard	Occurring? (Y/N)	Action required to minimise risk
Any article or substance falling or being ejected from the machine		
A rupture or disintegration		
Overheating or fire		
Unintentional or premature discharge of dust, gas, liquid, vapour or other substance		
Any part of the machine at a high or low temperature likely to cause injury		
Any other hazards?		

6 Emergency stop controls

Is a suitable design of emergency stop control located at appropriate control and operating points?

Identified control/operating points	Type of emergency stop control

7 Isolation

How is the machine isolated or locked off from the following energy sources (where relevant)?

Energy source	Method of isolation
Electricity	
Compressed air or gas	
Hydraulic	
Steam	
Other (eg gravity fall)	

8 Controls

	Yes/No	If no, what action is required?
Are controls clearly visible, identifiable and clearly marked where necessary?		
Are controls located to ensure that operators are not exposed to risk?		
Can the operator see any other person who may be exposed to risk when the controls are operated?		
Are there systems of work to ensure that no one is likely to be at risk when the machine starts?		
Are there suitable audible, visible or other warnings (if needed)?		

9 Workplace environment

	Yes/No	If no, action required?
Is there adequate natural and artificial light?		
Is lighting of controls satisfactory, without glare?		
Is lighting of parts of the machine that have to be viewed adequate?		
Is the workplace temperature in a range of comfort for operators?		
Is suitable seating required?		
Is there adequate space around the machine to allow safe and easy access?		
Is storage for machine parts and special tools needed?		
Are fire extinguishers needed close to the machine - if so, what type?		

10 Personal protective equipment (PPE)

	Yes/No	If no, action required?
Is PPE necessary?		
If yes, what type?		
Are operators aware that PPE is required?		
Do operators know how PPE should be worn?		
Is local storage necessary and provided?		
Is PPE subject to routine maintenance?		

11 Safety signs and warnings

Are adequate signs fitted to the machine as follows?

	Yes/No	If no, action required?
Hazardous surfaces		
Hazardous materials		
Hazardous parts or their movement		
Prohibited actions		
Correct operation		
Personal protective equipment (PPE)		
Emergency action		

APPENDIX 4

KEY STANDARDS FOR ENGINEERING WORKSHOPS

To help designers and manufacturers of new machines meet essential health and safety requirements (see page 34), a range of Transposed Harmonised Standards (BS ENs) has been developed to offer four levels of guidance:

'**A**' standards on basic safety concepts and design principles common to all machinery

'**B1**' standards on basic safety aspects such as safety distances and noise

'**B2**' standards on safety related devices such as guards and interlocking devices, and

'**C**' standards which interpret '**A**' and '**B**' standards and give safety requirements for a particular type or group of machines

'**pr EN**' standards are BS ENs under development, available from BSI (see page 81)

For machines used in engineering workshops '**C**' standards are planned for the commonest metalworking machines including mechanical, hydraulic and pneumatic presses and press brakes; grinding machines of all kinds; horizontal and vertical turning machines, both CNC and manually operated; machining centres, drilling, milling and boring machines of all types; and metalcutting saws and electro-discharge machines.

These standards will also be relevant to users of existing machinery to help them assess risks and decide whether safeguards are adequate.

Standard and title	Key contents and requirements
BS EN 292 : Part 1 : 1991 *Safety of machinery.* *Basic concepts, general* *principles for design*	1. Describes machinery hazards, defines safety terms, requires designers to assess risks, remove or control them. 2. All hazards from mechanical, electrical, thermal, noise, vibration, radiation, materials or ergonomic sources including any combination, have to be considered over the lifetime of the machine.
BS EN 292 : Part 2 : 1991 *Safety of machinery.* *Technical principles and* *specifications*	1. Describes methods to reduce risks by design. 2. Advises on selection, design and construction of safeguards for hazards which cannot be eliminated by design. 3. Describes information for use to be provided for users by suppliers.
BS EN 1050 : 1997 *Safety of machinery.* *Risk assessment*	1. Advises on the identification of hazards and provides criteria for assessing risks and selecting safety measures consistent with technical and economic restraints. 2. Outlines qualitative and quantitative risk assessment techniques and risk reduction measures.

BS EN 60204-1
Safety of machinery. Electrical equipment of machines -
Part 1: *General requirement*

1. Applies to low voltage equipment (1000vAC and 1500vDC, not exceeding 200Mz) from the point of supply to its use at the machine.
2. Covers protection against electric shock, measures to protect equipment against overcurrent, overspeed, overload and from the environment, restarting a hazardous operation from loss of power, general requirements, electrical controls, the accessibility, layout and identification of controls, ergonomic requirements for electrical controls, requirements for cabling, wiring, accessories, lighting, documentation and testing.

BS EN 953 : 1998
Safety of machinery. Guards (fixed, movable)

1. Contains definitions of different types of guard.
2. Sets requirements for when to use a particular type of guard and how to design guards to minimise hazards.

BS EN 1088 : 1996
Safety of machinery. Interlocking devices with and without guard locking

1. Defines basic concepts and general principles for interlocking devices controlling any power source.
2. Specifies requirements for electrical interlocking devices, and parts of guards which activate interlocking devices.

BS EN 294 : 1992
Safety of machinery. Safety distances to prevent danger zones being reached by upper limbs

1. Two values are given for reaching up to danger zones and two tables for reaching over protective structures.
2. Designer must decide what is to be used depending on whether situations are high or low risk.
3. Standard is not concerned with preventing climbing over barriers; 1800 mm may be sufficiently high for this.

BS EN 349 : 1993
Safety of machinery. Minimum distances to avoid crushing parts of the human body

1. Describes factors to be taken into account in the assessment to prevent crushing only.
2. Minimum gaps for whole body, leg, head, foot, toes, arm, hand, and finger are given in an illustrated table.
3. Annex A (Informative) illustrates three typical crushing zones at a milling machine table.

BS EN 626-1: 1995
Safety of machinery. Reduction of risks from hazardous substances emitted by machinery
- Part 1: *Principles and specifications for machine manufacturers*

1. Contains information on the types of hazards to be considered, with examples.
2. Annex A (Informative) provides examples of how exposure to hazardous substances may be reduced by eliminating or reducing risks.

BS 5304:1988
Safety of machinery

A non-harmonised standard containing many useful principles and examples of safeguarding for machinery which is being progressively replaced by harmonised standards.

USEFUL DEFINITIONS FROM BS EN 292: PART 1: 1991

Safety of a machine

The ability of a machine to perform its function, to be transplanted, installed, adjusted, maintained, dismantled and disposed of, under conditions of intended use, without causing injury or damage to health.

Hazard

A source of possible injury or damage to health.

Risk

A combination of the probability and degree of the possible injury or damage to health in a hazardous situation.

Risk assessment

A comprehensive estimation of the probability of possible injury or damage to health in a hazardous situation in order to select appropriate safety measures.

Danger zone

Any zone within and/or around machinery in which a person is exposed to risk of injury or damage to health.

Safety device

Device (other than a guard) which eliminates or reduces risk, alone or with a guard.

Interlocking device

Mechanical, electrical or other type of device, the purpose of which is to prevent the operation of machine elements under specified conditions (generally as long as guard is not closed).

Hold-to-run control device

Control device which initiates and maintains operation of machine elements only as the manual control (actuator) is actuated. The actuator returns automatically to the stop position when released.

Guard

Part of a machine specifically used to provide protection by means of a physical barrier.

Fixed guard

Guard kept in place (ie closed) either permanently (eg by welding) or by means of fasteners (screws, nuts etc) making removal/opening impossible without using tools.

Movable guard

Guard generally connected to the machine by mechanical means (eg hinges or slides) which can be opened without tools.

Adjustable guard

Fixed or movable guard which is adjustable as a whole or which incorporates adjustable part(s). The adjustment remains fixed during a particular operation.

Interlocking guard

Guard associated with an interlocking device so that:

▼ the hazardous machine function 'covered' by the guard cannot operate until the guard is closed

▼ if the guard is opened while hazardous machine functions are operating, a stop instruction is given

▼ when the guard is closed, the hazardous machine functions 'covered' by the guard can operate, but the closure of the guard itself does not initiate their operation. (To achieve this would require a control guard.)

Guard locking with interlocking

Prevents the opening of an interlocking guard until hazardous motions are stopped, and their restart until the guard is locked.

Safeguard

A guard or safety device.

Two-hand control device

Hold-to-run control device which requires at least the simultaneous operation of two manual controls (actuation) in order to trigger and maintain operation of the machine or machine elements, thus affording a measure of protection for the person operating the actuators.

Defining hazards

Hazards at machinery may arise from:

▼ mechanical movements, such as shearing

▼ electricity

▼ heat

▼ noise

▼ vibration

▼ radiation

▼ substances being used

▼ neglecting ergonomic principles in design

▼ combinations of hazards

▼ failures of energy supply

▼ missing safety measures, and

▼ being trapped inside.

Enabling (control) device

Additional manually operated control device used in conjunction with a start control and which, when continuously actuated, allows a machine to function.

Trip device

Device which causes a machine or machine elements to stop (or ensures an otherwise safe machine condition) when a person or a part of a body goes beyond a safe limit.

Trip devices may be:

▼ mechanically actuated, eg trip wires, telescopic probes, pressure sensitive devices etc

▼ non-mechanically actuated, eg photo-electric devices, devices using capacitive, ultra-sonic etc means to achieve detection.

APPENDIX 5

FIRE-RESISTANT MATERIALS FOR DIY SPRAY BOOTHS

Effective segregation, ventilation and prevention of ignition can be achieved in home-made spray booths, but with professional and competent advice.

Segregation

The separation or isolation should be fire resistant. Some examples of floor, wall and door construction that will provide a standard of half-hour fire resistance are:

Floors

Plain edge boarding on timber joists not less than 38 mm wide with a ceiling of 12.5 mm plasterboard and 12.5 mm gypsum plaster.

Tongued and grooved boarding not less than 16 mm thick on timber joists and not less than 38 mm wide with a ceiling of 12.5 mm minimum of plasterboard and a skim coat of gypsum plaster.

Plain edge boarding on timber joists not less than 38 mm wide with a ceiling of timber lath and plaster, the plaster at least 16 mm thick, covered on the underside with a 12.5 mm thickness of plasterboard.

Walls

100 mm brick (unplastered).

50 mm woodwool slabs plastered at least 12.5 mm thick on both sides, framed construction (non load-bearing).

Steel or timber studding with 12.5 mm portland cement plaster, portland cement/lime plaster or gypsum plaster on metal or timber lathing (non load-bearing conditions only).

Steel or timber studding with 9.5 mm thick plasterboard on each side with the exposed facing of the boarding plastered with 5 mm thick neat gypsum plaster (non load-bearing conditions only).

Where existing walls or partitions are not fire-resisting constructions, the standard can be achieved by adding 12.5 mm plasterboard; ensure that the joints between the overlap are formed over the supporting framework or otherwise suitably constructed.

Doors

Fit: The door should be reasonably straight and true and lie flush against the stop when closed; the gap between the door edge and the frame should not exceed 3 mm.

Door frame: Should have a rebate or stop not less than 25 mm deep; existing planted stops may be replaced or additional material screwed or pinned and glued on.

Door furniture: One pair of metal hinges, all parts of which are non-combustible and have a melting point not less than 800⁰.

Glazing: Any plain glazing should be replaced by, or backed with, 6 mm wire reinforced glass not exceeding 1.2m² in area and fitted with solid wood beading not less than 13 mm in cross section.

Flush doors*: 6 mm wallboard cover to both sides of the door; fixing to be 32 mm screws at approximately 300 mm centres, or annular nails at approximately 200 mm centres, driven into solid timber.

Panel, framed, ledged and braced doors*: Protection as for flush doors to both faces of the door; or, if protection against fire is needed from one side only, then 9 mm insulating board fixed to room-risk side of the door, as above, with the panels first made up with tightly fitting cutouts of plasterboard or solid wood.

*   *The importance of fixing cannot be over-emphasised. Additional material must be so* *fixed to the existing door that, under condition of fire where thermal movement is likely to take place between the door and protective material, the screws or nails are not stressed so that they are pulled out.*

Electrics

Unprotected electrical equipment must be kept outside spray booths.

Install lights outside booths and shine them through fixed and sealed fire-resisting wired glass panels.

Use only explosion protected electrical equipment inside the booth.

APPENDIX 6

RECORD OF EXAMINATION AND TEST OF LOCAL EXHAUST VENTILATION (LEV) PLANT

A suitable record containing at least the following particulars should be kept in respect of each thorough examination and test of LEV plant:

(a) Name and address of employer responsible for the plant

(b) Identification and location of the LEV plant, process, and hazardous substance concerned

(c) Date of last thorough examination and test

(d) Conditions at time of test; normal production or special conditions (eg maximum use, stood down)

(e) Information about the LEV plant which shows:

   (i) its intended operating performance for controlling the hazardous substance

   (ii) whether the plant now still achieves the same performance

   (iii) if not, the repairs required to achieve that performance

(f) Methods used to make judgement at (e)(ii) and (e)(iii) above (eg visual, pressure measurements, air flow measurements, dust lamp, air sampling, filter integrity tests)

(g) Date of examination and test

(h) Name, designation and employer of person carrying out examination and test

(i) Signature or unique authentication of person carrying out examination and test

(j) Details of repairs carried out.

APPENDIX 7
ANSWERS TO FREQUENTLY ASKED QUESTIONS ABOUT WORK IN ENGINEERING WORKSHOPS

QUESTION	ANSWER
Is it all right to work alone in the workshop?	It would not generally be reasonable for employers to permit employees to work alone, because there is usually some dangerous machinery about. (Fatal accidents have occurred following entanglements on centre lathes which may have been prevented had there been another person to switch off the machine and help the trapped worker.) However, if just low-risk work such as assembly or some cleaning is being planned, then provided other risks are minimised and a system of checking or line of communication established, it would be reasonable for an employee to work alone. See page 1 on how to manage safety.
What are the rules on smoking?	Smoking should not be permitted where flammable liquids are used, or anywhere near degreasing operations. Also, smoking may make any dust, fume, mist or vapour more harmful if inhaled. There is also a slight general health risk to non-smokers from tobacco smoke in the workshop and offices. Employers should develop a policy to minimise this risk. Rest room arrangements must protect non-smokers from discomfort caused by tobacco smoke.
Do I need to keep an accident book?	No, but you need to record details of accidents and occurrences which must be reported (see page 79).

You may use the DSS B1510 Accident Book, another book or a computer to record the following details:

▼ date and time of accident or occurrence

▼ full name and address of the person involved and the injury or condition suffered

▼ where the accident or occurrence happened

▼ a brief description of the circumstances

QUESTION	ANSWER

▼ in the case of a reportable disease the date of diagnosis, the occupation of the person concerned and the name or nature of the disease.

Keep the above information for at least three years.

What can young people do in the workshop?

Employment of children under 13 is forbidden, and children under this age should not normally be allowed in an engineering workshop. Children over 13 but under minimum school leaving age may only work under an official work experience scheme.

Young people under 18 are often exposed to risks to their health and safety when using work equipment as a consequence of their immaturity, lack of experience, and absence of awareness of existing or potential risks. Training and proper supervision of young people is therefore of particular importance.

If you employ a young person, the management regulations require you to assess risks to them before they start work, taking the above factors into account. You must use the risk assessment to determine whether the young person should be prohibited from certain work activities, except where necessary for their training. Young people should not for example be allowed to use high-risk lifting machinery unless they have the necessary maturity and competence and have successfully completed appropriate training. Your risk assessment may indicate that similar prohibitions are appropriate for high-risk machines such as presses, guillotines and milling machines

KEY REFERENCES: *Young people at work: A guide for employers* **HSG165 HSE Books ISBN 0 7176 1889 7;** *New and expectant mothers at work: A guide for employers* **(Second edition) HSG122 HSE Books ISBN 0 7176 2583 4**

QUESTION	ANSWER
	Sufficient training and adequate supervision should, of course, be provided for all work for all employees.
Do women have to be treated differently in the workshop?	In general no, but where work with lead or ionising radiations is concerned, their work needs careful assessment so that it can be managed properly to prevent undue risks to unborn children.
What notices do I have to put up?	▼ The only notice now required to be displayed is the Health and Safety Law poster (or an approved leaflet containing the same information can be given to each employee)
	▼ Electric shock and first-aid at work placards are no longer required to be displayed by law but contain advice for use in emergencies.
	▼ The above posters may be obtained from HSE Books in an encapsulated format.
What breaks are workers entitled to, and what hours of work are required?	A worker is entitled to an uninterrupted break of 20 minutes when daily working time is more than six hours. Additionally, a worker is entitled to a rest period of 11 consecutive hours between each working day and to an uninterrupted rest period of not less than 24 hours within each 7-day period.
	The weekly working time for a worker must not exceed 48 hours per week, averaged over a 17-week period. Workers may individually or collectively sign an agreement with their employer to work over this limit. The normal hours of night workers must not exceed an average of 8 hours for each 24 hours over a 17-week period.

KEY REFERENCE: *A guide to Working Time Regulations* (free)
DTI: 08701 502 500

QUESTION

Are eye tests required for users of VDUs?

ANSWER

Users, and those to become users, can request an eye and eyesight test that you have to pay for, if they are your employees. If the test shows they need glasses specifically for their VDU work, you have to pay for a basic pair of frames and lenses.

Users are entitled to further tests at regular intervals after the first test, and in between if they are having visual difficulties which may reasonably be considered to be caused by their VDU work.

If users' normal glasses for other work are suitable for VDU work you don't need to pay for them. You don't have to pay for fancy frames, or lenses. Eye and eyesight testing is not an entitlement for the self-employed.

When setting up a system for providing users with eye and eyesight tests, these points might help:

▼ contact a number of opticians and ask what they charge for tests and basic glasses

▼ ask if they will come to the firm to test the users

▼ ask for standard information about each user they test, if they need glasses for VDU work and when they should be re-tested

▼ tell users what arrangements you have made

▼ make sure users understand what you will and won't pay for (eg tinted lenses, glasses for non-VDU purposes are not your responsibility).

KEY REFERENCE: *Working with VDUs* INDG36(rev1) HSE Books (single copy free; ISBN 0 7176 1504 9 for priced packs of 10)

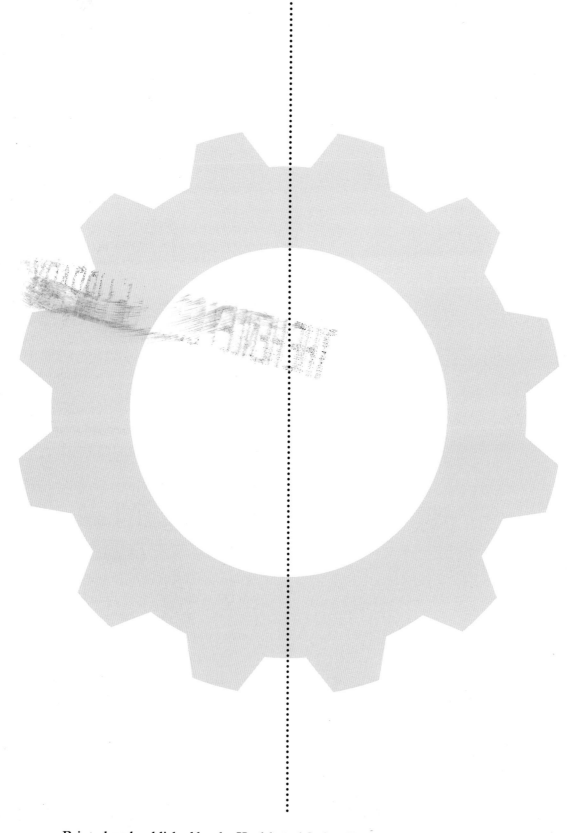

Printed and published by the Health and Safety Executive   C50   02/04